HOW TO DO

BETTER

HAIRCOLORING

the complete textbook of successful tinting,

lightening, corrective techniques and hair care

including 124 professional case histories

TO YOU...

the professional hairdresser
whose skilled hands
coax beauty into being

whose soaring imagination
creates new visions
of beauty

CLAIROL TECHNICAL
TRAINING CENTERS

NEW YORK CITY
Statler Hilton Hotel
7th Ave. and 33rd St.
Second Office Floor
212 957-3040

Philadelphia, Pa.
1011 Chestnut St.
Room #903
215 MArket 7-6775

Chicago, Ill.
17 North State St.
Room #1800
312 FInancial 6-8765

Newark, New Jersey
100 Washington St.
201 MArket 3-2453/2454

Boston, Mass.
69 Boylston Place
617 DEvonshire 8-9226

San Francisco, Calif.
207 Powell St.
415 EXbrook 7-6052

Los Angeles, Calif.
6015 Santa Monica Blvd.
213 HOllywood 2-1242

Toronto, Ontario
40 Hayden St., E.
924-6687-88

Montreal, Quebec
768 Sherbrooke St., W.
514 UNiversity 6-9581

This is the CLAIROL INSTITUTE
OF HAIRCOLORING in New York, the largest
school of its kind in the world. Here professional
hairdressers come from all over America
for free instruction in the latest haircoloring
techniques. See column for the addresses and
phone numbers for the branches in other cities.

CLAIROL ANSWERING SERVICES ARE LOCATED IN THE FOLLOWING CITIES TO PROVIDE IMMEDIATE TECHNICAL HELP AT ALL TIMES. AREA CODES PRECEDE EACH NUMBER.

Albany, New York 518-HE 4-3612	**Kansas City, Missouri** 816-GR 1-6770	**Pittsburgh, Pa.** 412-GR 1-0605
Albuquerque, New Mex. 505-CH 7-1135	**Knoxville, Tennessee** 615-523-7077	**Portland, Oregon** 503-CA 2-1953
Atlanta, Georgia 404-JA 4-1936	**Louisville, Kentucky** 502-JU 3-0683	**Providence, R. I.** 401-JA 1-3522
Baltimore, Maryland 301-SA 7-5500	**Los Angeles, California** 213-HO 2-1242	**Rochester, New York** 716-GR 3-7928
Birmingham, Alabama 205-879-1412	**Miami, Florida** 305-371-6510	**Salt Lake City, Utah** 801-IN 7-4760
Boston, Massachusetts 617-DE 8-9226	**Memphis, Tennessee** 901-JA 3-1205	**San Antonio, Texas** 512-PE 3-1601
Buffalo, New York 716-TL 6-4160	**Milwaukee, Wisconsin** 414-BR 3-5805	**San Diego, California** 714-BE 4-5046
Chicago, Illinois 312-FI 6-8765	**Nashville, Tennessee** 615-AL 6-8216	**San Francisco, California** 415-OR 3-3600
Cincinnati, Ohio 513-621-2444	**Newark, New Jersey** 201-MA 3-2453	**San Jose, California** 408-CY 5-7144
Cleveland, Ohio 216-MA 1-5710	**New Orleans, La.** 504-524-5901	**Seattle, Washington** 206-MA 4-6860
Dallas, Texas 214-RI 1-5225	**New York, New York** 212-957-3040	**St. Louis, Missouri** 314-PA 5-1234
Denver, Colorado 303-244-9017	**Omaha, Nebraska** 402-346-4032	**Syracuse, New York** 315-HO 3-4533
Detroit, Michigan 313-WO 1-5529	**Philadelphia, Pa.** 215-MA 7-6775	**Washington, D.C.** 202-DE 2-8000
Houston, Texas 713-CA 8-5405	**Phoenix, Arizona** 602-274-3527	**Worcester, Massachusetts** 617-PE 7-7419

TABLE OF CONTENTS

FOREWORD

Since its first publication in 1953, more than 1,000,000 copies of "How To Do Better Haircoloring" have been distributed to beauty salons, beauty schools, and libraries throughout the world.

Clairol is proud that through the pages of this book, hundreds of thousands of hairdressers have become proficient and expert haircolorists.

"How To Do Better Haircoloring" remains the most authoritative and complete textbook in the field. It is an integral part of the curricula of hundreds of beauty schools, and the information contained in it is used as a basis for testing the haircoloring qualifications of hairdressers in many states.

This latest edition has been brought up to date with all the latest information on haircoloring products and techniques.

These methods and techniques have been developed over a period of years in the Clairol Institute of Haircoloring, and have been carefully tested in Clairol's network of Training Centers and in beauty salons throughout the country.

"How To Do Better Haircoloring" is divided into two parts. The first part covers the techniques of haircoloring, lightening, corrective work and care of tinted and toned hair. The second part includes 124 Professional Case Histories which analyze and give the solutions to problems most encountered by hairdressers throughout the country.

The book should be used both as a text to be read from beginning to end and as a reference book to be referred to constantly in your day-to-day work.

The beginning haircolorist will find it an unerring guide to the very profitable art of haircoloring. The experienced haircolorist will find it most valuable as a refresher and as a guide to new advanced techniques and products.

Used properly, "How To Do Better Haircoloring" can become your most valued professional tool.

If you encounter a problem that the book does not answer, do not hesitate to call your local representative or write or phone the Clairol Institute of Haircoloring.

CHAPTER 1

HAIRCOLORING
METHODS

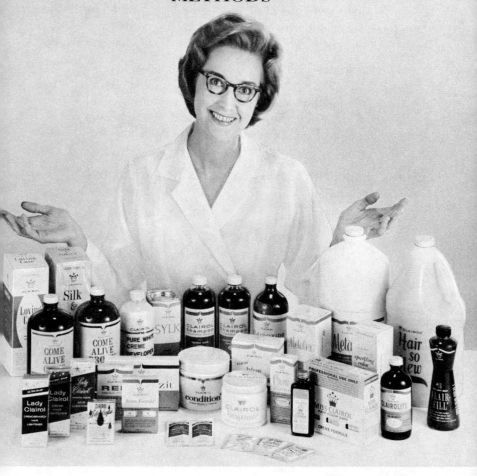

THERE ARE many ways to color hair and thousands of products which are used for coloring. Haircoloring in itself is not new. We don't know if Eve hennaed her hair, but almost since the beginning of time women have tried to improve on nature. (Then, as now, the feminine trait of being dissatisfied with "born" hair color was apparent.) A background follows about the history of haircoloring and how it evolved from artificial-looking shades to the natural-looking beauty that makes today's haircoloring undetectable.

1

A Dip Into History

ANCIENT DAYS

In ancient Egypt henna (a red dye derived from a small shrub) and indigo were favored for coloring. Sage and camomile were also used. The dark-haired Romans of Caesar's time, who were dazzled by the fair beauty of their captive Teutons, bleached their hair with saffron, red arsenic, nutshells and ashes of plants. The golden beauties of the Renaissance wet their hair with soaps and exposed it to the sun or mixed alum, black sulphur and honey to turn into honeyed blondes.

A NEW INVENTION

In 1885 paraphenylenediamine was discovered for use in haircoloring. This new compound was used alone or in combination with metallic salts. At the turn of the century bleaching and dyeing became popular with actresses but the results were looked upon as socially unacceptable, possibly because they were so obvious.

CLAIROL DISCOVERY MARKS NEW ERA IN HAIRCOLORING

In 1932 Clairol introduced the Oil Shampoo Tint. Tint was mixed

with peroxide or peroxide compounds, plus small amounts of natural oils, and a thick solution was created which could be applied with a swab or brush and would not run. It produced natural-looking colors and haircoloring became frank—and nice.

GIANT STEP BY CLAIROL

In 1950 Clairol completely revolutionized haircoloring—both as to method and result—with the introduction of Miss Clairol Hair Color Bath, a one-step method. *For the first time* tinting and lightening were made possible in one operation. Now it was possible to tint hair to a lighter color without pre-lightening, a scientific and technical stride that reached out and touched almost every woman who wanted to do something about the color of her hair. (Today statistics show that one woman out of three colors her hair.) This one-step method cut down the time necessary for coloring hair, made haircoloring less expensive and more easily available to the average customer. The haircolorist was able to double and triple her daily output of work over the time-consuming old-fashioned methods.

Three Kinds of Haircoloring In Use Today

Haircoloring today falls into three general classifications:

1. Permanent haircoloring which lasts until hair grows out.

2. Semi-permanent haircoloring which lasts until it wears off or washes out (after repeated shampoos).

3. Temporary haircoloring which stays on hair until shampooed out.

The professional tinter must understand how each method and type of coloring product works and its effect upon the hair.

Permanent Haircolorings

There are two kinds of permanent haircolorings—penetrating tints and coating tints. Each remains in the hair until the hair grows out or is changed by another process such as lightening or a tint remover treatment. It cannot be *washed* out with soap and water. It is used to cover gray, to change a hair shade completely or to brighten or deepen an existing shade.

1. PENETRATING TINTS

Almost all permanent haircoloring today is done with the use of oxidation or penetrating tints.

These tints penetrate through the outer (cuticle) layer of the hair and into the cortex (center layer) where they are oxidized or developed by the peroxide to insoluble pigments deposited in the same pattern as the natural pigments. At the same time, some of the natural hair pigment is lightened by the lightening action in the products. These pigments

3

(in layman's language) dominate the existing pigment. Color is distributed where nature intended it to be (inside the hair). This gives a natural-looking color. Penetrating tints require that a Patch Test be given 24 hours before each application.

Superiority of penetrating tints

1. Natural-looking color that does not fade or turn into "off shades."

2. Color goes *inside* hair shaft (does not coat) and is distributed in same pattern as natural hair pigments.

3. Tinting action stops when hair is rinsed so hair does not darken after application.

4. Conditioning oils work beneficially on hair shaft, keeping it supple and in healthy condition so that hair texture is often *improved*.

5. Are compatible to permanent waving chemicals. Hair may be tinted *after* a permanent.

THE PENETRATING TINTS IN THE CLAIROL LINE ARE:

Miss Clairol Hair Color Bath which deposits color in the hair and at the same time lightens hair.

Salon Formula Oil Shampoo Tint which deposits color but does not lighten simultaneously.

Clairol Creme Toner which are delicate shades in the Oil Shampoo Tint formula and are used in high-fashion blonding. Hair must be pre-lightened before Creme Toner is applied.

Red Fashion Colors which are dramatic reds that may be applied to natural or pre-lightened hair. Oil Shampoo Tint Formula.

2. COATING TINTS

The coating tints take on the outside of the shaft on the cuticle layer, obliterating light and producing unnatural colors and a dull, crayony look. Their use today is comparatively small (usually in the home rather than in the beauty shop). However, the professional operator must recognize them since, after their use, hair must frequently be reconditioned before successful application of tints or lighteners or permanent waves is possible. There are two kinds of coating tints—the vegetable extracts and the metallic dyes.

Vegetable Extracts—Plant extracts are not used now for hair tinting. The so called white henna is not a plant extract. It is magnesium carbonate with a strong alkaline reaction which tends to damage hair with prolonged use.

Metal Salt Dyes and Metal Compounds—The metal salt dyes are called progressive dyes or color restorers because each subsequent application increases the coating on the hair and hair color becomes progressively darker.

These metallic dyes have a tendency to fade into peculiar colors. Those that contain lead turn purple. The dyes containing silver turn green, and those containing copper turn red. They are in little use today.

Henna Compound Dyes or Rastiks—The henna compound dyes are mixtures of metallic salts with organic intermediates such as pyrogallol. The colors achieved with these compounds are more natural looking than those obtained with the metallic salts alone, but no lightening of the hair is possible, and they fade easily. They are discolored by cold-wave permanents. Hair treated with these compounds cannot be lightened or tinted until the metallic salts have been removed.

Semi-Permanent Colorings

An entirely new category of haircoloring has recently been developed by Clairol: semi-permanent haircoloring that is a gently self-penetrating color which requires no peroxide developer and fades naturally. It keeps its color through five shampoos or more (usually about a month) and requires the Patch Test.

There are three types:

1. Semi-permanent color which covers gray completely but does not affect the remaining pigmented hair—a Clairol exclusive.

2. Semi-permanent color to make gray hair more beautifully gray—another Clairol exclusive.

3. Semi-permanent color to add color and highlights to hair without gray.

Features of semi-permanent haircoloring

1. Color gently penetrates so the effect is natural, lifelike.

2. Color can't rub off, wash off or rinse off, because it is *in,* not *on,* the hair.

3. Longer-lasting results than with rinses.

4. Eliminates retouching. Color is applied each time the same way—there is no obvious line of demarcation.

5. Simple to use.

6. Can be removed if desired.

7. Hair will return to natural color in from 4 to 6 weeks if reapplication is not desired.

8. Improved condition and high sheen of the hair.

CLAIROL SEMI-PERMANENT HAIRCOLORING PRODUCTS ARE:

Loving Care Hair Color Lotion which colors *only* the gray to match the natural hair shade so the effect is of even, fresh color.

Silk & Silver Hair Color Lotion which makes gray hair more beautifully gray, gives it an even tone and banishes yellow discoloration.

Sparkling Color Hair Color Lotion which is used on hair untouched by gray to brighten and highlight the natural shade or add a touch of new color.

Temporary Haircolorings

Temporary colorings deposit color on the outside of the hair shaft and have no lasting effect on the color of the hair. They are generally removed by shampooing, but some of the temporary types are resistant to one or two shampoos. Temporary haircolorings are used to intensify natural haircoloring, to add highlights to the natural shade, to cover a limited amount of gray and to eliminate yellowish shades from white and gray hair. There are three kinds of temporary haircolorings:

1. RINSES

Rinses are the satisfactory method for women who want to highlight hair color, give it another color cast, add beauty or eliminate yellowish shades from white or gray hair. They are a valuable introduction to permanent haircoloring.

Advantages of rinses:

1. Give a temporary color effect for women who do not wish to go in for permanent tints.

2. Condition hair—make it manageable, give it body.

3. Wash out easily.

4. No Patch Test is required.

5. Give sparkle, highlights, life to dull, mousey hair.

6. Blend in a certain amount of gray with natural shade.

Clairol rinses are called the "Come Alive" series and consist of:

Come Alive Gray   (4 shades to highlight gray)

Come Alive Brown   (highlights brown)

Come Alive Blonde   (highlights blonde)

Come Alive Red   (highlights red)

2. HIGHLIGHTING SHAMPOOS

Some shampoos combine the action of a rinse with that of a shampoo to give highlights and slight color tones to the hair. These shampoos generally contain certified colors. Other highlighting shampoos do not contain coloring matter but do contain a bleaching agent. They cannot be strictly termed coloring since they remove color instead of adding it.

Their action is due to solid peroxide compounds present in a soap or detergent base. A still third category is the mixture of coloring, developer and shampoo which highlights, brightens and blends in first gray hairs.

Miss Clairol used as a quick glamour treatment (see Chapter 4) has the action of a highlighting shampoo.

3. POWDERS, CRAYONS, HAIR COLOR CREMES AND SPRAYS.

Powders are practically extinct with the exception of metallic powders which are used to apply temporary hair streaks.

Hair Crayons are used to retouch newly grown hair between tint treatments.

Hair Color Cremes are used mostly for theatrical make-up. They rub off easily because of their greasy base.

Hair Color Sprays are mostly gold and silver and are applied from aerosol containers for extra exotic effects.

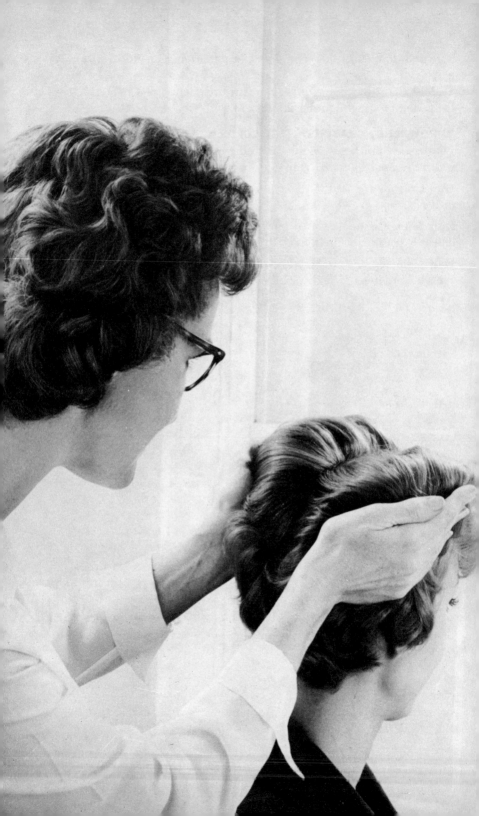

CHAPTER 2

GETTING
READY
TO TINT

THE REASON a woman comes to you for haircoloring is that she depends upon your professional skill to give her natural-looking haircolor. If it is her first time, much as she might want to color her hair, she may have a few qualms. Your warm manner and interest in her will reassure her, and the professional way you conduct the preliminary consultation will inspire faith in your judgment and skill.

To assure the most successful results in haircoloring a preliminary consultation with your patron is necessary. Spend a few extra minutes studying her coloring and the texture of her hair. Discuss with her whether she wishes to brighten her natural color, make a drastic change or cover gray. Usually you will find a patron comes with an idea of the shade she wishes. Refer to your Clairol Color Chart·to make sure you know exactly what she has in mind. If her selection would not be becoming to her skin tone and present haircoloring, tactfully make alternate suggestions of more flattering shades. But do not *insist* on your color recommendation. You want her happy, satisfied and coming back.

During the consultation you will want to accomplish the following:

1. **Select the hair shade**

2. **Examine your patron's scalp**

3. **Discuss upkeep with her**

4. **Make a Preliminary Patch Test**
   (If it is 24 hours before you plan to tint—otherwise make an appointment for the Patch Test so that not more than 24 hours will elapse between the Patch Test and the full head or retouch application.)

Rules to Follow in Making Color Selection

1. **Good lighting** is imperative for good color selection. A stark north light is best in which to evaluate color. If color selection is made at night (or if natural daylight is not available), use incandescent rather than flourescent light (which tends to give hair a bluish cast).

2. **Clean, dry hair** is essential in evaluating color so make sure your

9

patron's hair is not soiled or wet. Hair always appears darker under these conditions and might influence you to select too dark a shade.

3. Do not look down on hair. Raise the strand and observe color by pushing the hair up with the hand against the scalp. To study the color properly, look through the hair toward the light to see the depth of color as well as the highlights.

4. When matching hair color, observe the hair nearest the scalp at the back of the head. This is where it is darkest.

5. Have a Clairol Color Chart available which shows you the range of colors and gives you the name and number of each color. Since the color shown on the chart is the shade achieved on pure white hair, you must then decide on the special formula which will give the desired color when combined with the patron's natural pigment.

6. Consider skin tones. In general, women with olive skins or skins with a yellowish cast will find the ash colors and darker colors most becoming. Fair or creamy complexioned women have the whole range of hair color at their disposal and can be as daring as they wish. Women with a florid or pinkish cast can choose dark or light colors, but they look their prettiest in colors with little or no red.

7. Gray-haired women are apt to want to go back to their pre-gray color, but because there has been a lightening of skin tones as well as hair, a shade or two lighter than their original color is more becoming. The lighter colors are far more flattering and younger looking.

Specific steps in color selection depend largely on the properties of the particular products you are using. Further instructions on color selection appear in the chapters on different methods of tinting.

MAKE A CAREFUL SCALP EXAMINATION

Examine the patron's scalp carefully for cuts, abrasions, eruptions or open wounds. If any of these exist, postpone tinting. No hair preparation should ever be applied if any of these conditions exist.

DISCUSS UPKEEP

"How much will it cost?" "How often will I need a retouch?" "Is it a nuisance?" These are questions every woman considers before she has her hair colored. If she doesn't ask, be sure to tell her how much her first treatment will cost and how often she should have her hair retouched. Point out the cost of the touch-up depends on the color chosen. A dramatic color change, for instance, will mean more frequent retouches than one closer to her own natural shade. Or gray hair tinted to match the natural pigment will need less frequent touch-ups than if a decided change is made. Upkeep factors might very well determine her choice of shade. She will appreciate your frankness and will quickly sense your interest.

Hypersensitivity and the Patch Test

It is a well known fact that certain individuals, for undetermined reasons, may be allergic or hypersensitive to foods, drugs, cosmetics, or any other substances or materials that are harmless to the multitude. These relatively few persons subject to such reactions are said to be allergic or hypersensitive. The method employed to detect such skin hypersensitivity is the Preliminary Patch or Skin Test, as prescribed for hair colorings under the Federal Food, Drug and Cosmetic Act.

Accordingly, for the relatively few persons susceptible to this product, no express or implied warranty is given as to freedom from ANY asserted unfavorable effect or result which may be ascribed to its use.

How To Give a Patch Test

Make this Preliminary Patch or Skin Test 24 hours before every application (full head or retouch) to ascertain whether a person is hypersensitive or allergic to the product.

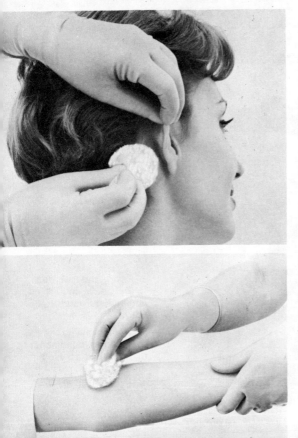

1. With bland soap and water, wash an area about the size of a quarter on the innerfold of the elbow or behind either ear and extending partly into the hairline. (Dry by patting with absorbent cotton.)

2. Prepare the test solution by mixing a few drops of the color of product to be used in the tinting with an equal number of drops of Clairoxide or Pure White Creme Developer (at least 6 drops of each if applicable.) If a mixture of colors is to be used in the actual tinting, the test solution must be prepared to duplicate that tinting mixture.

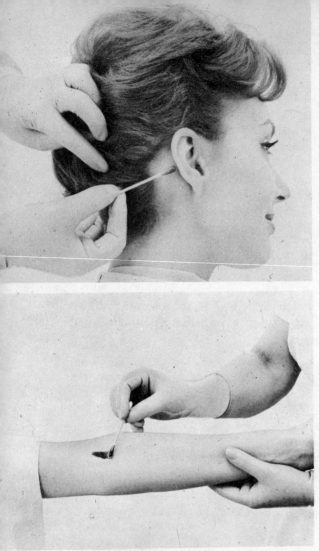

3. With an absorbent cotton-tipped applicator, apply the test solution to the area previously cleansed.

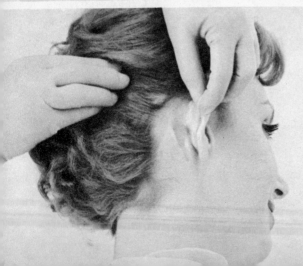

4. Permit the test area to dry. Leave uncovered and undisturbed for 24 hours.

5. Then, examine the test area. If found negative, the mixture used in the Patch Test must be applied **immediately.**

If any reddening of the skin, burning, itching, swelling, irritation, eruption, or any other abnormal reaction is experienced in or around the test area at any time during the test period, then the person is predisposed to the preparation and must not use it. This preparation should not be applied to the hair if the scalp or adjacent areas show evidence of any abrasion, eruption or other abnormal or diseased condition. This product must not be used on eyelashes or eyebrows. This admonition has been included because we have no adequate or safe method of predetermining the presence of hypersensitivity of the more delicate orbital tissues.

Now You're Ready to Tint

You and your patron have chosen the haircoloring shade, and the Patch Test has shown no allergy to the tint. You're now ready to proceed.

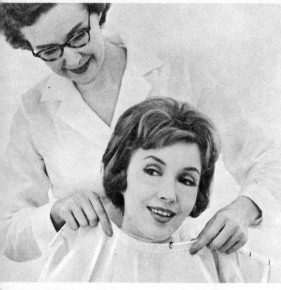

1. Prepare the patron. Protect her from being splashed by the tint preparation. Since it can permanently discolor clothing, ask her to remove her blouse or dress to prevent staining. Protect her with a towel and a plastic or rubber cape.

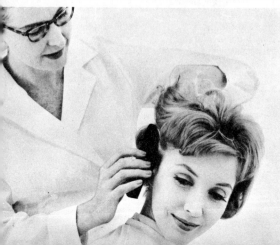

2. Make a careful scalp examination. Make certain there are no abrasions, eruptions or open wounds. If they are present, do not proceed with tinting.

13

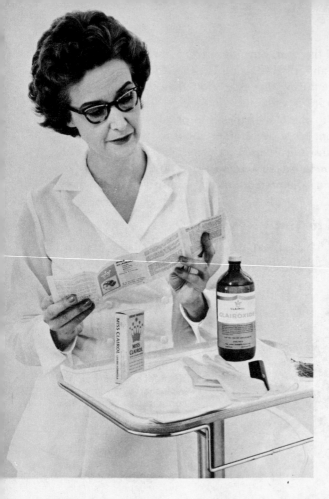

3. Assemble your materials. Neatness indicates professionalism—a ready line-up of materials assembled before you start helps you work efficiently.

THIS CHECK LIST WILL SERVE AS A GUIDE:

Towels
Shampoo cape
Rubber gloves (to be worn at all times during tinting and lightening treatments)
Dishes (Glass or plastic dishes should be used in tinting and lightening. Metal dishes should never be used.)

Tint brushes (The type of brush used for both lightening and toning is most important in the final result.
You should use only a narrow fiber brush since nylon brushes have a tendency to irritate the scalp and cause hair damage.)

Miss Clairol or Lady Clairol Applicator
Swab sticks
Combs
Cotton
Clairol, the colorfast shampoo
Clairol tint product
Clairol lightener
Clairol developer
Clairol Color Chart

The Preliminary Strand Test
PREVIEW OF YOUR COLOR SELECTION

The only sure way to tell how each individual's hair will react to color is the Preliminary Strand Test. No two heads of hair have exactly the same balance of red and brown pigment, the same porosity, the same resistant spots. The Strand Test takes all guesswork out of color selection and timing requirements. It also gives your patron assurance to see how carefully and expertly you are working to give her the exact color she has in mind. A Strand Test must also be made before application of a lightener.

THIS PRELIMINARY STRAND TEST WILL HELP YOU DETERMINE THE FOLLOWING:

1. Whether proper color selection has been made.

2. The proper length of time to leave the lightener or tint on the hair.

3. Whether the hair has been previously treated with either a permanent wave, lightener, tint, metallic dye, compound henna or rinse. Thus you will foresee any possibility of breakage or discoloration. When any of these conditions is evident, do not tint or lighten without first reconditioning and then retesting the hair.

4. If the general condition of the hair is not good, the test will show where porous areas exist and enable you to foresee unsatisfactory results such as streaked or dark ends.

A Preliminary Strand Test for Tinting or Lightening is Given in the Following Manner:

1. Mix small quantities of material to be used.
a. If a tint is used (Miss Clairol, Clairol Creme Toner or Red Fashion Color), mix equal parts of color (or mixture of colors) selected and Pure White Creme Developer or Clairoxide.
b. If a semi-permanent color is used (Loving Care, Silk & Silver or Sparkling Color), no developer is required.
c. If a lightener is used (Clairolite, Ultra-Blue Lady Clairol, Instant Whip Lady Clairol or Lady Clairol Whipped Creme) mix 1 part lightener with 2 parts Pure White Creme Developer or Clairoxide. Add Lightening Booster or Protinator if used. Always check directions which come with product for exact proportions.

15

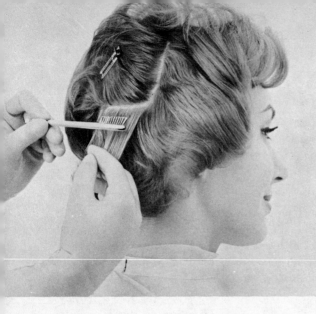

2. Apply the mixture to a full strand of hair. Allow it to develop until the desired shade has been reached. Follow explicit timing instructions which come with each product.

3. Wash and dry the test strand and examine results. In regular tint application if strand is almost correct, leave on longer for a deeper shade; less time for a lighter shade. But if color is very different from the shade desired, select another color and make another Strand Test.

Discoloration in the Strand Test indicates the presence of foreign elements, and corrective steps must be taken. For specific directions see Chapter 16—"Reconditioning Hair" and Case Histories from 20 through 30.

Clairol Plastic Applicator

The Clairol Plastic Applicator makes the application of tint or lightener much more efficient, easier, faster, more easy to control. Mixture will not drip or dry out. It takes the place of dish, comb, brush or swab. The applicator holds the mixture, and the nozzle, like the rattail comb, is used for parting.

How to Mix in Applicator

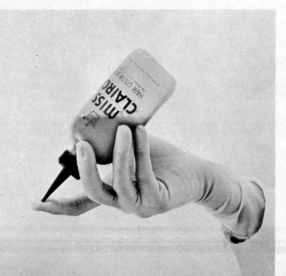

Pour tint and developer into special Clairol applicator. Then cover the top of the applicator with your gloved hand and turn over gently four or five times. If you are using Miss Clairol Creme Formula, the mixture will turn into a thick, heavy creme. The more you turn the bottle, the thicker the creme becomes. Test thickness by squeezing small portions gently through the nozzle.

1. For tinting, part hair in four equal sections according to diagram. White lines indicate parallel partings for tint application. If you use plastic applicator to apply tint, hold applicator firmly in the palm of your hand, and make partings with the tip of the nozzle.

2. Pick up strand of hair with your free hand, and hold away from the head at such an angle as to expose roots or new growth.

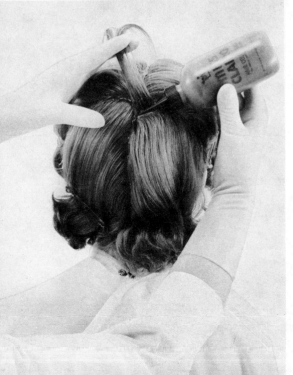

3. Now place the nozzle point over the new growth. Gently squeeze the applicator, and apply the mixture liberally. Part hair and apply mixture in applicator from left to right. Make new parting on return motion from right to left.

17

The Use and Care of the Developer

Penetrating tints and lighteners must be mixed with hydrogen peroxide which is a *developer*. Final results are only as good as the developer you use. Ordinary peroxide is a very unstable compound. *For best results Clairoxide or Pure White Creme Developer, Clairol's two peroxides, should be used.*

Both are pure, fresh, stable 20-volume hydrogen peroxide. (Anything higher, such as 30- or 40-volume, is too strong; tends to damage or irritate the patron's hair and scalp. Anything lower than 17-volume is too weak.) *Purity* of Clairol's developers is another assurance of good results. *The slightest amount* of impurities in a developer could cause the tint or lightener to froth, making it impossible to apply evenly and give proper results.

**Pure White
Creme
Developer**

Clairol's newest developer formula is Pure White Creme Developer. It was determined by the U. S. Testing Company to be the most stable product of its kind. You will find its creamy "stay-put" consistency will not run or drip, making application easier, faster and more comfortable to your patron. Moreover, it prevents drying out and thus eliminates the need for repeated application.

Pure White Creme Developer is guaranteed pure, is of the desired 20-volume strength and contains ingredients which condition the hair, leaving it strong and lustrous. In tinting, greater color intensity and better coverage on resistant hair are achieved. It accelerates lightening action, cutting lightening time, a real boon when working with over-lightened hair. You will find when working with hair that's delicate, over-lightened, tinted or over-processed that Pure White Creme Developer is almost a *must* if hair is to be left in good condition.

Clairoxide

Clairoxide is a pure, stable 20-volume peroxide in liquid form. It may be used interchangeably with Pure White. *Mix developer with tint or lightener immediately before application.* Do not allow the prepared mixtures to stand any length of time or they will lose their strength. **Warning:** Never store any tint or lightener after it has been mixed with a developer; the container may burst. Any mixture remaining after a treatment *must* be discarded.

Keeping Tint Records

A personalized service, valuable to the beauty salon and reassuring to your patron, is the Tint Record. Keep a complete record of each treatment—especially a tint. It is not only a permanent record that you can refer to in future colorings but is another sure, professional touch that makes a patron feel you're interested in *her.*

CLAIROL TINT RECORD

NAME					TELEPHONE			
ADDRESS					REFERRED BY			
TYPE OF HAIR – SILKY ☐	WIRY ☐	FINE ☐	COARSE ☐	HARSH ☐	SOFT ☐	STRAIGHT ☐	CURLY ☐	
NATURAL COLOR		SHADE DESIRED			PERCENTAGE OF WHITE			
WHAT COLORINGS OR BLEACHES HAVE BEEN USED PREVIOUSLY								
IS PATRON ALLERGIC TO ANY FOOD OR PRODUCT								
GENERAL CONDITION OF HAIR AT PRESENT TIME								
GENERAL CONDITION OF SCALP AT PRESENT TIME								
RESULT OF PREDISPOSITION TESTS								

DATE	TREATMENT GIVEN	T.	H.	A TIME	D TIME	RESULTS	OPERATOR

Storing Your Materials

As tinting materials are affected by heat, light, and cold, great care should be taken in storing them. Select a room with an even, normal temperature, not exposed to sunlight. Keep your tint supplies away from radiators and other heating elements. Have your merchandise well marked and keep a record of your inventories so that you will not run out of needed materials.

Do's and Don't's for Success
with Lightening and Haircoloring

Do's

1. Make sure that the Clairol product you select is the one best suited to the results you wish.

2. Before starting on lightening or tinting treatment have all products and utensils ready to your hand.

3. Avoid using metal bowls and containers in all lightening and tinting work. Use plastic applicator, glass or plastic bowls and measuring utensils.

4. Wear rubber gloves to protect hands in applying lighteners and permanent tints.

5. Be sure patron's clothing is well protected with towel and large plastic or rubber cape before applying lightener or tint.

6. Make a *Patch Test* 24 hours before each and every coloring full head or retouch treatment. This is required by law. (See page 11.)

7. Before application of lighteners or tints make a *Preliminary Strand Test* for timing and color.

8. Make frequent strand tests as soon as color starts to develop or lightening action begins.

9. Prepare your lightening or coloring mixture *immediately before* application.

10. Keep a complete record card of treatments for every patron.

11. Use fresh, stable 20-volume hydrogen peroxide ... Clairoxide or Clairol Pure White Creme Developer.

12. Shampoo hair thoroughly after lightening with Clairol Blue Shampoo.

13. Handle lightened or tinted hair gently. Do not rub scalp when shampooing or pull hair when combing after treatment.

14. Recondition highly lightened hair regularly.

15. Towel dry hair thoroughly before applying Clairol Creme Toner. Hair should be only slightly moist so as not to dilute the delicate tint.

16. When lightening hair, leave lightening mixture on only long enough to reach the correct stage of color and porosity. Make frequent strand tests.

17. Always read, or reread, and follow directions that come with Clairol products. They have been tested by experts to give you best results.

Don't's

1. Haircoloring must never be used to tint eyebrows or eyelashes. Don't allow tint or lightener to contact area around the eyes.

2. Never save any unused mixtures of tint and developer or of lighteners. Any remaining mixture must be discarded.

3. Never proceed with hair tinting or lightening if there are abrasions, eruptions or open wounds on scalp. Examine scalp carefully first.

4. Don't rub or massage scalp when applying or rinsing out tints or lighteners.

5. Don't pre-shampoo before lightening or applying Miss Clairol Hair Color Bath. Apply to dry hair.

6. Don't apply lighteners or haircoloring to hair coated with metallic dyes, compound hennas or hair restorers. First recondition hair to remove coating. (See Chapter 16)

7. Don't use ordinary shampoos on tinted or toned hair; they may remove color. Use one of the Clairol special shampoos: Clairol Shampoo, Blue for Lightened and Toned Hair, or Clairol Shampoo, Green for Tint and lasting rinse users.

8. Don't use an ordinary creme rinse or setting lotion after a haircoloring treatment; it may strip color. Clairol Hair So New acts as rinse, setting lotion and conditioner in one.

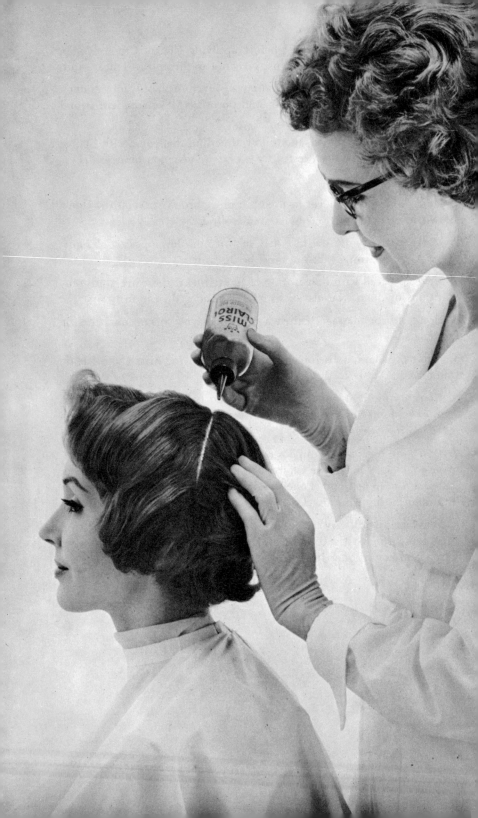

CHAPTER 3

MISS CLAIROL
HAIR COLOR BATH
CREME FORMULA

MISS CLAIROL HAIR COLOR BATH, the amazing one-step haircoloring method originated by Clairol, does four things: lightens, colors, conditions and shampoos.

Miss Clairol both tints and lightens the hair, so that the lighter, brighter tones may be obtained without pre-lightening. With Miss Clairol, young patrons can enjoy a dramatic, glamorous change of color, while older patrons can retain becoming, natural-looking color while they completely cover any amount of gray. A darker-than-natural shade may be achieved with Miss Clairol if desired, of course. So natural-looking are the results that haircoloring is undetectable.

Miss Clairol Creme Formula

Miss Clairol Creme Formula is the latest and recommended formula of Miss Clairol Hair Color Bath. Mixed with a developer this liquid becomes an easy-to-work-with creme when stirred or shaken. It "stays put," does not drip, run down the strand or dry out. Miss Clairol Regular retains its liquid form when mixed with the developer. Both are applied the same way. The wearing quality is greater with Creme Formula.

miss clairol color selector

IF THE NATURAL HAIR SHADE IS

TONE	COLOR NO.	COLOR NAMES (from light to dark)	BLONDE Result obtained	RED Result obtained
EXTRA-DRAB-1	30	FLAXEN BLONDE (Pale Baby Blonde)	Light pale blonde.	Light red.
DRAB-1	40	TOPAZ (Champagne Blonde)	Light blonde.	Lighter red.
GOLD-1	41	GOLDEN APRICOT (Honey Blonde)	Medium golden blonde.	Slightly lighter red.
DRAB-2	42	MOONGOLD (Medium Ash Blonde)	Dark ash blonde.	Drabber red.
GOLD-2	43	SUN BRONZE (Reddish Blonde)	Medium reddish blonde.	Red with gold high lights.
RED-1	33	FLAME (Bright Red Red)	Light bright red.	Brighter red.
RED-2	44	COPPERTONE (A Real Copper)	Light auburn.	Red with copper highlights.
RED-3	45	SPARKLING SHERRY (Light Auburn)	Medium auburn.	Red with medium auburn tones.
DRAB-3	46	CHESTNUT BROWN (Light Brown)	Light brown.	Red with brown tones.
RED-4	47	RED GINGER (Reddish Brown)	Reddish brown.	Reddish brown.
DRAB-4	57	COFFEE BROWN (Rich Medium Brown)	Medium brown.	Medium brown.
DRAB-5	48	SABLE BROWN (Dark Brown)	Dark brown.	Dark Brown.
DRAB-6	51	BLACK VELVET (Gleaming Black)	True black.	True black.
LIGHT DRAB TONER	49	ERMINE	Ermine and Starlight are not used alone but in conjunction with the other Miss Clairol shades to minimize undesirable natural red tones. If Ermine is not sufficient, use Starlight which is twice as effective.	
DARK DRAB TONER	50	STARLIGHT		

Results obtained also apply to tinted hair, except when a lighter shade is desired. Then tinted portion of hair must be lightened before Miss Clairol is used.

13-fashion-right colors
IF THE NATURAL HAIR SHADE IS

BROWN Result obtained	GRAY & WHITE Result obtained	BLACK Result obtained	MAXIMUM LIGHTENING ACTION
Lighter shade with blonde highlights.	Light pale blonde with darker hair lightened and toned.	Lighter bright brown.	Up to 9 shades.
Lighter shade with decided gold or red highlights.	Light blonde with darker hair lightened to blend in.	Bright brown.	Up to 7 shades.
Lighter shade with golden blonde highlights.	Golden blonde with dark hair lightened to blend in.	Brown with very gold highlights.	Up to 5 shades.
Lighter golden brown.	Ash blonde.	Brown with gold highlights.	Up to 3½ shades.
Light reddish brown.	Reddish blonde.	Brown with reddish highlights.	Up to 4 shades.
Bright red.	Light bright red.	Brown with bright red highlights.	Up to 6 shades.
Coppery red.	Bright, light copper-red.	Brown with copper-red highlights.	Up to 4½ shades.
Medium auburn.	Medium auburn.	Brown with auburn highlights.	Up to 3½ shades.
Light brown.	Light brown.	Medium brown.	Up to 3 shades on very dark hair only.
Reddish brown.	Reddish brown.	Reddish brown.	Up to 3 shades on very dark hair only.
Medium brown.	Medium brown.	Medium dark brown.	Up to 2 shades on very dark hair only.
Dark brown.	Dark brown.	Very dark brown.	Up to 1-2 shades on very dark hair only.
True black.	True black.	Truer, richer black.	None.

SPECIAL NOTE

TONAL VALUE OF COLOR: The column "Tone" classifies Miss Clairol colors by depth of color and highlights created by each. Drab colors have no red or gold highlights. Gold colors have only gold highlights. Red colors have only red highlights. Tone numbers indicate the intensity of the color—the higher the number, the darker the color.

LIGHTENING ACTION OF COLORS: The last column on the Chart titled "Maximum Lightening Action" indicates the maximum shade that each color can lighten when applied to dark hair. When the Miss Clairol color chosen is near the natural shade, the amount of lightening action is automatically less.

Miss Clairol Color Selector Chart

Miss Clairol Colors

There are 13 Miss Clairol colors and 2 special drabbers. On the Miss Clairol Color Selector Chart you will see these colors arranged by groups; the drabs, the golds, the reds. Within each group the colors range from light to dark, beginning with the lightest color. This arrangement will help you in lightening or darkening colors because change in intensity may be made by adding the next lighter or darker color in the same group.

Each Miss Clairol color has these identifications, all of which appear on the Miss Clairol Color Selector Chart:

1. **Color number**—for ordering and stockkeeping purposes.

2. **Color name**—used in advertising and for customer identification.

3. **Descriptive name**—which tells the color each shade will produce on white hair.

4. **Tonal classification**—which indicates whether shade has drab, red or gold tones.

5. **Lightening action**—which tells the degree of lightening action in each color.

Miss Clairol on White Hair

The best way to observe the results of Miss Clairol colors is to see their effect on pure white hair. When they are applied to hair that is not completely pure white there is a variation in color due to the natural pigmentation. Shades pictured in the Miss Clairol Color Selector are the results on pure white hair.

Miss Clairol on Dark Hair

Miss Clairol colors on dark hair, of course, will have a different effect than they do on white hair. It is on dark hair that you must consider the lightening action of Miss Clairol. The darker the hair, the greater the lightening action. The closer the natural shade is to the Miss Clairol color, the less Miss Clairol will lighten. As Miss Clairol colors deepen, their lightening action lessens.

Let Us Consider the Effects of Each Miss Clairol Color on Pure White Hair and on Dark Hair

THE BLONDE COLORS

FLAXEN BLONDE (Pale Baby Blonde) is the lightest, drabbest shade.
On White Hair it produces the lightest, palest drab blonde shade with no red or gold tones.
On Dark Hair it will lighten up to 9 shades and while it lightens will reduce red or gold tones. The final shade depends upon how dark the hair was originally.

TOPAZ (Champagne Blonde) is a light drab blonde.
On White Hair it produces a light pale blonde with no red or gold tones.
On Dark Hair it will lighten up to 7 shades. While lightening, it will reduce red and gold tones. The final shade depends upon how dark the hair was originally.

GOLDEN APRICOT (Honey Blonde) is a golden blonde several shades deeper than Topaz.
On White Hair it produces a golden blonde shade.
On Dark Hair it lightens up to 5 shades. It adds golden highlights as it lightens.

SUN BRONZE (Reddish Blonde) is deeper than Golden Apricot. It contains more gold and some red.
On White Hair it produces a light to medium rich, reddish golden blonde.
On Dark Hair it lightens about 4 shades and adds reddish gold tones.

MOONGOLD (Medium Ash Blonde) is a drab blonde at least four shades darker than Topaz and just a little darker than Sun Bronze.
On White Hair it ranges from medium to dark ash blonde.
On Dark Hair it lightens up to $3\frac{1}{2}$ shades. While lightening it reduces the reds and golds, like Topaz, but to a greater degree because it contains more drab coloring.

THE RED COLORS

FLAME (Bright Bright Red) is the lightest shade in the red group.
On White Hair it produces a very vivid color and may not look completely natural. The white haired woman should only use this color when she wants an intense, dramatic red.
On Dark Hair Flame lightens hair up to 6 shades producing a light, bright red.

COPPERTONE (A Real Copper) is several shades deeper than Flame.
On White Hair it produces a light auburn. It is more natural looking than Flame on white hair.
On Dark Hair it lightens about 4½ shades, producing a light, coppery red.

SPARKLING SHERRY (Light Auburn) is an auburn with light to medium depth, several shades deeper than Coppertone.
On White Hair it produces a light to medium auburn shade.
On Dark Hair it lightens about 3½ shades, producing a medium auburn.

RED GINGER (Reddish Brown) is several shades deeper than Sparkling Sherry with more brown in it.
On White Hair it produces a light, reddish brown.
On Dark Hair it lightens about 3 shades and adds reddish brown tones.

THE BROWN COLORS AND BLACK

CHESTNUT BROWN (Light Brown) is a light brown with no red or gold. A color similar to Moongold, it is at least three shades darker.
On White Hair it produces a light, drab brown.
On Dark Hair it lightens 2½ to 3 shades and at the same time produces lustrous brown tones.

COFFEE BROWN (Rich Medium Brown) is a brown several shades deeper than Chestnut. It has no red or gold.
On White Hair it produces a rich medium brown.
On Dark Hair it produces a rich medium brown. It lightens *only* dark brown or black hair several shades.

SABLE BROWN (Dark Brown) is a dark brown with no red or gold tones. It is several shades lighter than Black Velvet.
On White Hair it produces a lustrous dark brown.
On Dark Hair it produces a lustrous dark brown. It lightens *only* black hair one or two shades.

BLACK VELVET (Gleaming Black) is a true black with no red, gold or purple.
On White and Dark Hair it produces pure, gleaming black. Has no lightening action whatsoever.

Color Selection with Miss Clairol

When selecting a Miss Clairol color, take into account that Miss Clairol *lightens* as well as *colors*. For this reason, you must consider *both* the lightening value and the coloring value of each color.

KEY TO MISS CLAIROL COLOR SELECTION

1. **To match the natural shade of hair and cover gray:**
Select the color closest to the natural shade.

To Match	NATURAL SHADE		MISS CLAIROL SHADE		RESULT
	Light Brown	+	Miss Clairol Chestnut	=	Light Brown

2. **To lighten natural shade and cover gray:**
Select a color *lighter* than the natural shade but one containing enough color to produce the desired shade on gray and sufficient lightening action to lighten dark pigment.

To Lighten	NATURAL SHADE		MISS CLAIROL SHADE		RESULT
	Light Brown	+	Miss Clairol Topaz	=	Dark Blonde

3. **To darken natural color and cover gray:**
Select a color darker than the natural shade with enough color to give depth desired.

To Darken	NATURAL SHADE		MISS CLAIROL SHADE		RESULT
	Light Brown	+	Miss Clairol Sable	=	Dark Brown

Effect on natural gray or white hair. The shade produced on gray hair will be only as deep as the color used. (See page 32 for detailed information about Miss Clairol on gray hair.)

Each Miss Clairol color has its own depth. A dark shade cannot be produced by choosing a lighter shade and leaving it on for a longer period of time. If, in the finished result, hair appears too light, color selection was incorrect and a deeper color must be used.

Lightening Action of Miss Clairol Colors

Miss Clairol *lightens* as it tints. Therefore you must consider the degree of lightening action in each color. The following chart shows the *Lightening Action by Shades* on natural hair.

LIGHTENING ACTION   BY SHADES
(on natural hair)

UP TO

30 Flaxen Blonde	**9**	
40 Topaz	**7**	
33 Flame	**6**	
41 Golden Apricot	**5**	
44 Coppertone	**4½**	
43 Sun Bronze	**4**	
42 Moongold	**3½**	
45 Sparkling Sherry	**3½**	
47 Red Ginger*	**3**	
46 Chestnut Brown*	**3**	
57 Coffee Brown*	**2**	
48 Sable Brown*	**1**	*Lightens only when applied to very dark hair.

51 Black Velvet
(no lightening action)

SHADE DEFINITION.

The definition of a *shade* is a degree of color between two basic colors. (For example, the difference between light brown and medium brown is *several shades*.)

WHAT TO EXPECT:

Therefore you cannot expect that Topaz (with the lightening action of 7 shades) will lighten dark brown hair to a color as light as champagne blonde. It will lighten dark brown hair *7 shades* to about a color slightly darker than Moongold. Should a dark-haired patron wish a color like Topaz, she cannot use Miss Clairol without *pre-lightening* first.

Miss Clairol Colors by Tone Value

In selecting colors or in mixing them to achieve the results desired, it is necessary to consider the *tone* value of each color. Each Miss Clairol color falls into the category of drab, gold or red tone.

Drab colors have no red or gold highlights.

Gold colors have only gold highlights.

Red colors have only red highlights.

The following chart shows Miss Clairol colors in their tonal categories. The colors are arranged by tone values and by depth, beginning with the lightest color. Tone numbers indicate the intensity of the color —the higher the number, the darker the color.

COLORS BY TONAL VALUES

DRABS

Extra Drab 1   Flaxen Blonde

1	Topaz	3	Chestnut Brown	5	Sable Brown
2	Moongold	4	Coffee Brown	6	Black Velvet

REDS		GOLDS	
1	Flame	1	Golden Apricot
		2	Sun Bronze
2	Coppertone		
		SPECIAL DRABBERS	
3	Sparkling Sherry	1	Ermine
4	Red Ginger	2	Starlight

COLORS MAY BE LIGHTENED OR DEEPENED WITHOUT CHANGING THEIR TONE VALUE

To deepen or lighten colors without changing their tone values:

1. If Topaz on pure white hair is a little too light, it can be deepened by adding a small amount of the color next in depth to it in the same tone. To 1¾ oz. Topaz add ¼ oz. Moongold and 2 oz. developer. Since both tint colors are drab, adding Moongold does not change the tone value. It merely produces a deeper shade.

2. If Moongold has been used and the results are a little too deep, reverse the procedure and add Topaz. Mix 1¾ oz. Moongold with ¼ oz. Topaz and 2 oz. developer.

Tone values may be changed as colors are lightened or deepened.

For example, if Topaz used on pure white hair is a little too light and a little too drab, it should be mixed with Golden Apricot, the next color in the gold tones. This will deepen the color and add a little gold. Mix 1¾ oz. Topaz with ¼ oz. Golden Apricot and 2 oz. developer.

Ermine and Starlight

Two special Miss Clairol colors are Ermine and Starlight. They are not to be used alone but are special blenders designed to be mixed with other Miss Clairol colors for drabbing purposes.

Use the following proportions: 1½ oz. Miss Clairol color and ½ oz. of Starlight or Ermine to drab any Miss Clairol color.

Starlight is *twice as concentrated* as Ermine. It may be used on hair with a great deal of red pigment where more drabbing is required. Therefore the final color will be drabber and appear darker.

When either of these drabbing colors is used in conjunction with a Miss Clairol color, a proportionate quantity should be added to the test solution in the Preliminary Patch and Strand Tests.

Silver Drops

Miss Clairol colors may also be made drabber by the addition of a Clairol product called Silver Drops. Silver Drops, a specially prepared, highly concentrated drabber, reduces and drabs red or gold tones. Add from 3 to 15 drops to Miss Clairol. The deep colors require 15 drops for adequate drabbing; the lighter colors require less. To ascertain the correct number of Silver Drops, make a Strand Test, using Silver Drops in the tint mixture. A Preliminary Patch Test is necessary when Silver Drops is added to any formula.

Note—Never Use Alone—Never use Ermine, Starlight or Silver Drops alone on gray, white or "pepper-and-salt" hair as a rinse. They will lighten whatever dark pigment still exists and cause discoloration.

Miss Clairol on Hair Mixed with Gray

When hair is gray, two factors influence the final color; difference in pigmentation and amount of gray. Because of these two factors, seldom will the same Miss Clairol color look alike on two different heads of hair.

1. DIFFERENCE IN PIGMENTATION.

Some women have a great deal of red pigmentation, and no matter what color you use on them, you will always find red highlights coming through. Women with little red in their hair will always finish with a somewhat drabber version.

2. AMOUNT OF GRAY IN HAIR.

The amount of gray influences the final color. For example, three patrons, all with some red pigmentation in their hair, are tinted with Moongold with these results:

a. The patron with no gray, who is matching her natural hair shade will finish with a shade with *some* red highlights.

b. The patron who has 50% gray will finish with *less* red in her hair than the one who has no gray at all since the gray hair does not contain red pigmentation.

c. The patron whose hair is white will have the true Moongold shade with *no* red highlights.

Remember, the more *white* in the hair, the less gold and red in the final shade.

HOW TO ACHIEVE DRAB COLORS
WHERE RED PIGMENTATION EXISTS

Often, because of the presence of red in the hair, drab colors will not finish drab. The red tones can be reduced by the use of Ermine and Starlight, Clairol's two special drabbers.

Resistance in gray hair

Occasionally there is the exceptional patron with gray hair extremely difficult to cover. To get complete coverage on this unusual type of hair follow one of these procedures.

1. Mix 2 ounces of tint with 1½ ounces of developer. Allow this to remain on the hair a sufficient length of time to develop its full color.

2. Mix 1 part of Miss Clairol Topaz with 2 parts of developer and apply to the new growth as a pre-softener. Allow this mixture to remain on the hair for 15-20 minutes. At the end of that time, simply remove the excess tint with a towel. DO NOT SHAMPOO. Then apply Miss Clairol in the usual manner.

3. A diluted lightener mixture may be used as a pre-softener. Any of the three Lady Clairol lighteners or Clairolite may be used for pre-softening. Note that the following pre-softening formulas are mixed with a greater amount of developer.

a. Instant Whip or Lady Clairol Whipped Creme Hair Lightener highly diluted with developer. For example: ¼ oz. Instant Whip to 1-2 ozs. Clairoxide or Pure White Creme Developer.

b. Ultra-Blue Lady Clairol or Clairolite highly diluted with developer. For example: ¼ oz. Ultra-Blue Lady Clairol to 1 oz. Clairoxide or Pure White Creme Developer. Allow the mixture to remain on the hair from 5 to 20 minutes. This is not long enough to cause any appreciable change in color, but it makes the hair more receptive to the tint color. Then shampoo.

Miss Clairol Confidential Formulas

The ability to mix colors skillfully is one of the most important keys to a successful haircoloring business. Miss Clairol colors may be blended to create an unlimited number of personalized shades.

Combinations to give a wide range of color selections are provided in the Confidential Formulas which follow. Proper usage of these combinations assures each patron of an individualized service. The colors you mix for her cannot be reproduced at another salon unless she has the exact formula you have blended for her.

Color mixing is especially important when matching your patron's natural shade since frequently it is a blend of colors rather than just one color.

Use these Confidential Formulas to do more subtle haircoloring and to add exciting possibilities to the colors you offer your customers. All results are based on white or gray hair.

MISS CLAIROL CONFIDENTIAL FORMULAS
DRAB SHADES

NO.	MIXING FORMULA	RESULTS
1.	1 oz. Flaxen Blonde 2 oz. Clairoxide or Pure White Creme Developer	Light Flaxen Blonde (Increases the lightening action of Flaxen Blonde)
2.	1 oz. Flaxen Blonde 1 oz. Topaz 2 oz. Clairoxide or Pure White Creme Developer	Lighter and drabber than Topaz
3.	2 oz. Flaxen Blonde 3 capfuls of Moongold 2 oz. Clairoxide or Pure White Creme Developer	Slightly deeper than Flaxen Blonde
4.	1½ oz. Flaxen Blonde ½ oz. Moongold 2 oz. Clairoxide or Pure White Creme Developer	Extra Deep Flaxen Blonde
5.	1 oz. Flaxen Blonde ½ oz. Moongold 1½ oz. Clairoxide or Pure White Creme Developer	Extra Drab Light Ash Blonde
6.	1 oz. Flaxen Blonde 1 oz. Moongold 2 oz. Clairoxide or Pure White Creme Developer	Light Ash Blonde
7.	1 oz. Flaxen Blonde 1 oz Chestnut Brown 2 oz. Clairoxide or Pure White Creme Developer	Ash Blonde (Very light brown)
8.	1 oz. Topaz 2 oz. Clairoxide or Pure White Creme Developer	Light Topaz (Increases the lightening action of Topaz)
9.	2 oz. Topaz 3 capfuls of Moongold 2 oz. Clairoxide or Pure White Creme Developer	Deep Topaz (Slightly deeper than Topaz)

10.	1½ oz. Topaz ½ oz. Moongold 2 oz. Clairoxide or Pure White Creme Developer	Extra Deep Topaz
11.	1 oz. Topaz ½ oz. Moongold 1½ oz. Clairoxide or Pure White Creme Developer	Light Ash Blonde (Lighter than Moongold)
12.	1 oz. Topaz 1 oz. Moongold 2 oz. Clairoxide or Pure White Creme Developer	Ash Blonde (Lighter than Moongold)
13.	1 oz. Moongold 2 oz. Clairoxide or Pure White Creme Developer	Light to Medium Ash Blonde (Lighter than Moongold and with a little gold tone)
14.	1½ oz. Moongold ½ oz. Starlight 2 oz. Clairoxide or Pure White Creme Developer	Medium Ash Blonde (Slightly drabber than Moongold)
15.	1 oz. Topaz 1 oz. Chestnut Brown 2 oz. Clairoxide or Pure White Creme Developer	Dark Ash Blonde (Very light brown)
16.	1 oz. Chestnut Brown 2 oz. Clairoxide or Pure White Creme Developer	Extra Light Ash Brown
17.	1 oz. Moongold ½ oz. Chestnut Brown 1½ oz. Clairoxide or Pure White Creme Developer	Light Ash Brown (Slightly deeper than Moongold)
18.	1 oz. Moongold 1 oz. Chestnut Brown 2 oz. Clairoxide or Pure White Creme Developer	Very Light Brown (Lighter than Chestnut Brown)
19.	1 oz. Coffee Brown 1 oz. Moongold 2 oz. Clairoxide or Pure White Creme Developer	Light Brown
20.	1½ oz. Chestnut Brown ½ oz. Starlight 2 oz. Clairoxide or Pure White Creme Developer	Light Brown (Drabber than Chestnut Brown)

21.	1½ oz. Chestnut Brown ½ oz. Coffee Brown 2 oz. Clairoxide or Pure White Creme Developer	Neutral Brown
22.	1 oz. Sable Brown 1 oz. Moongold 2 oz. Clairoxide or Pure White Creme Developer	Deep Neutral Brown
23.	1 oz. Chestnut Brown ½ oz. Sable Brown 1½ oz. Clairoxide or Pure White Creme Developer	Light Medium Brown
24.	1 oz. Sable Brown 1 oz. Chestnut Brown 2 oz. Clairoxide or Pure White Creme Developer	Medium Brown (Slightly lighter than Coffee Brown)
25.	1½ oz. Coffee Brown ½ oz. Starlight 2 oz. Clairoxide or Pure White Creme Developer	Medium Brown (Drabber than Coffee Brown)
26.	1½ oz. Sable Brown ½ oz. Starlight 2 oz. Clairoxide or Pure White Creme Developer	Dark Brown (Drabber than Sable Brown)

GOLDEN SHADES

NO.	MIXING FORMULA	RESULTS
1.	1 oz. Topaz 1 oz. Golden Apricot 2 oz. Clairoxide or Pure White Creme Developer	Light Golden Blonde
2.	1 oz. Golden Apricot 2 oz. Clairoxide or Pure White Creme Developer	Golden Blonde (Lighter than Golden Apricot)
3.	2 oz. Topaz 2-3 capfuls Flame 2 oz. Clairoxide or Pure White Creme Developer	Light Gold Titian Blonde

4.	1 1/2 oz. Golden Apricot 1/2 oz. Ermine 2 oz. Clairoxide or Pure White Creme Developer	Golden Blonde (Slightly less golden than Golden Apricot)
5.	1 oz. Topaz 1 oz. Sun Bronze 2 oz. Clairoxide or Pure White Creme Developer	Light Reddish Blonde (Lighter than Sun Bronze)
6.	1 oz. Topaz 1/2 oz. Coppertone 1 1/2 oz. Clairoxide or Pure White Creme Developer	Light Titian Blonde
7.	1 oz. Sun Bronze 1 oz. Golden Apricot 2 oz. Clairoxide or Pure White Creme Developer	Dark Golden Blonde (Little deeper and redder than Golden Apricot)
8.	1 oz. Golden Apricot 1 oz. Moongold 2 oz. Clairoxide or Pure White Creme Developer	Extra Dark Golden Blonde (deeper than Golden Apricot)
9.	1 oz. Golden Apricot 1/2 oz. Coppertone 1 1/2 oz. Clairoxide or Pure White Creme Developer	Light Golden Auburn
10.	1 oz. Moongold 1 oz. Sun Bronze 2 oz. Clairoxide or Pure White Creme Developer	Extra Light Titian Brown

RED SHADES

NO.	MIXING FORMULA	RESULTS
1.	1 oz. Topaz 1 oz. Flame 2 oz. Clairoxide or Pure White Creme Developer	Medium Titian Blonde

2.	1 oz. Flame 2 oz. Clairoxide or Pure White Creme Developer	Bright Titian Red (Lighter than Flame)
3.	1 oz. Sun Bronze 2 oz. Clairoxide or Pure White Creme Developer	Titian Blonde
4.	1 oz. Golden Apricot 1 oz. Flame 2 oz. Clairoxide or Pure White Creme Developer	Golden Titian
5.	1 oz. Sun Bronze 1 oz. Flame 2 oz. Clairoxide or Pure White Creme Developer	Deep Titian Red
6.	1 oz. Golden Apricot ¼ oz. Sun Bronze ¼ oz. Flame 1½ oz. Clairoxide or Pure White Creme Developer	Light Golden Auburn
7.	1 oz. Golden Apricot 1 oz. Coppertone 2 oz. Clairoxide or Pure White Creme Developer	Golden Auburn (Ligher than Coppertone, redder than Sun Bronze)
8.	1 oz. Golden Apricot 1 oz. Sparkling Sherry 2 oz. Clairoxide or Pure White Creme Developer	Deep Golden Auburn
9.	1 oz. Flame 1 oz. Coppertone 2 oz. Clairoxide or Pure White Creme Developer	Bright Auburn
10.	1 oz. Coppertone 2 oz. Clairoxide or Pure White Creme Developer	Light Auburn (Lighter than Coppertone)
11.	½ oz. Golden Apricot 1 oz. Coppertone 1½ oz. Clairoxide or Pure White Creme Developer	Medium Golden Auburn

12. 1 oz. Flame   Red Auburn
        1 oz. Sparkling Sherry
        2 oz. Clairoxide or
        Pure White Creme Developer

13. 1 oz. Coppertone   Coppery Auburn
        1 oz. Sparkling Sherry
        2 oz. Clairoxide or
        Pure White Creme Developer

14. 1 oz. Sun Bronze   Very Dark Reddish Blonde
        ½ oz. Red Ginger
        1½ oz. Clairoxide or
        Pure White Creme Developer

15. 1 oz. Sun Bronze   Light Reddish Brown
        1 oz. Red Ginger
        2 oz. Clairoxide or
        Pure White Creme Developer

16. 1 oz. Coppertone   Light Red Brown
        1 oz. Red Ginger   (Lighter and redder than
        2 oz. Clairoxide or   Red Ginger)
        Pure White Creme Developer

17. 1 oz. Sparkling Sherry   Red Brown
        1 oz. Red Ginger   (Slightly lighter and
        2 oz. Clairoxide or   redder than Red Ginger)
        Pure White Creme Developer

18. 1½ oz. Coffee Brown   Medium Red Brown
        ½ oz. Sparkling Sherry
        2 oz. Clairoxide or
        Pure White Creme Developer

19. 1½ oz. Sable Brown   Deep Red Brown
        ½ oz. Sparkling Sherry
        2 oz. Clairoxide or
        Pure White Creme Developer

When mixing colors, you can save the unused portions for later use if no developer has been added to them. To do so, combine colors in one bottle. Be sure to mark the combination on the bottle.

How to Make Miss Clairol Shades Lighter
LIGHT COLORS

If you desire the lighter, more glamorous shades, the Miss Clairol colors that lend themselves best to these are: Flaxen Blonde, Topaz, Golden Apricot, Sun Bronze, Flame, Coppertone. Although these colors have their own lightening action, lightening can be increased by *doubling the amount of the developer* or by *adding the Clairol lightener, Instant Whip Lady Clairol.*

As little as two capfuls of Lady Clairol may be added for a slight increase in lightening action. For a greater increase in lightening action, the following formulas can be used:

1. 1¾ oz. Miss Clairol
   ¼ oz. Lady Clairol (4 capfuls Lady Clairol cap)
   2¼ oz. Clairoxide or Pure White Creme Developer

2. 1½ oz. Miss Clairol
   ¼ oz. Lady Clairol
   2 oz. Clairoxide or Pure White Creme Developer

3. 1 oz. Clairol
   1 oz. Lady Clairol
   3 oz. Clairoxide or Pure White Creme Developer

A sample formula might be 1 oz. Flame, 1 oz. Lady Clairol, 3 oz. Clairoxide. This will produce a lighter, brighter shade than Flame mixed with equal parts of Clairoxide. These formulas may be used as a guide. Further variations will enable you to increase the subtle color variations you can create.

When you use only one or two capfuls of Lady Clairol, use the standard amount of Clairoxide (that is, 1 part Clairoxide to 1 part Miss Clairol), but increase the Clairoxide when you use ¼ oz. Lady Clairol or more.

The proportion is 1 part Clairoxide for each part of Miss Clairol, plus 2 parts Clairoxide for each part Lady Clairol .

Sometimes when using Flaxen Blonde or Topaz you will find that the Lady Clairol, while it increases the lightening action, decreases the color value so that the toning effect is not as great. If this occurs the tone can be made drabber by adding Ermine, Starlight or Silver Drops.

LIGHTENING DARK COLORS

Occasionally, even with the deeper colors, a slight increase in lightening action may be desired. This is done by mixing the Miss Clairol color with a lighter color in the *same tone value.* Example. Sable with Moongold.

Or the addition of two to four capfuls of Lady Clairol with Chestnut Brown, Red Ginger or Coffee will result in lightening the shade.

GRAY HAIR COVERAGE WHEN LIGHTENING COLORS

When mixing Lady Clairol with Miss Clairol, remember while you increase the lightening action, you decrease the coloring action. This means that women with gray hair get less coverage than they ordinarily would with the regular Miss Clairol mixture.

Therefore, as the amount of gray in the hair increases, decrease the amount of Lady Clairol you use. With 50% or more of gray hair you cannot mix Lady Clairol with Miss Clairol and expect complete, full color value.

With all these mixtures, the application procedure is the same as for Miss Clairol. No pre-shampoo is needed.

Miss Clairol Color Dial Helps You Choose the Perfect Tint Formula...Automatically

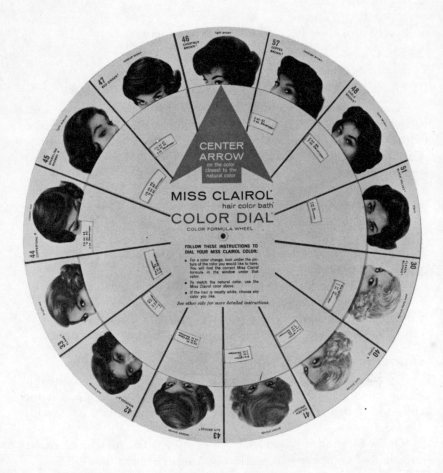

In selecting a formula you now have learned that you must take three things into consideration: the shade of your patron's hair, the shade you want it to be and the color and lightening capacity of the Miss Clairol shade. To help you, Clairol has developed the Miss Clairol Color Dial.

Thirteen shades of hair are reproduced on a circular disc—the same shades as those your patron sees on the Miss Clairol Color Selector Chart. The dial is worked by moving a large arrow. You simply point the arrow to the present shade of your patron's hair, and for a color change look under the color desired. The correct Miss Clairol formula appears in a small, boxed window. This compact dial has the answer to 156 different tinting situations.

Quick, easy, dependable, you will find it a great timesaver. However, do not use the Color Dial exclusively. You will often come across problems the Color Dial cannot answer. You'll find answers to all your hair coloring situations in this workbook.

Mixing Miss Clairol Hair Color Bath

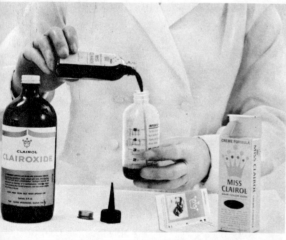

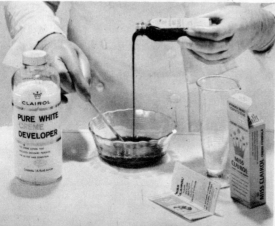

Mix 1 bottle (2 oz.) Miss Clairol with equal parts (2 oz.) of Clairoxide or Pure White Creme Developer in plastic applicator or glass or plastic dish. Never use a metal dish.

How to Apply Miss Clairol Hair Color Bath

PRELIMINARY

1. Select the color or colors to be used. (See pages 24 and 25.)

2. Give Preliminary Patch Test 24 hours before tinting. (See page 11.)

3. Make a Preliminary Strand Test to preview results. (See page 14.)

4. Examine the scalp to see that there are no cuts or abrasions. Do not apply Miss Clairol or any other hair preparation while they exist.

Application to Virgin Hair

There are two methods of applying Miss Clairol when tinting hair for the first time.

METHOD A. Is used when the Miss Clairol color is close to the natural shade of hair.

METHOD B. Is used when the Miss Clairol color is several shades lighter than the natural shade of hair.

Miss Clairol is always applied to dry hair. Do not shampoo before application. However, if hair is extremely soiled or has a heavy rinse build-up and shampooing is necessary, dry hair thoroughly before applying Miss Clairol.

METHOD A.

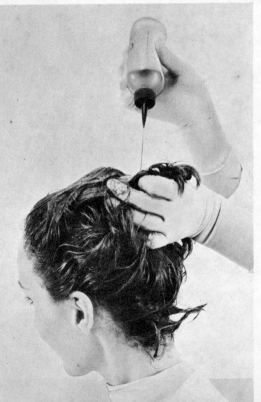

1. Apply the Miss Clairol mixture directly to the hair. Use the applicator, a swab or a brush. Make sure every strand is thoroughly saturated.

44

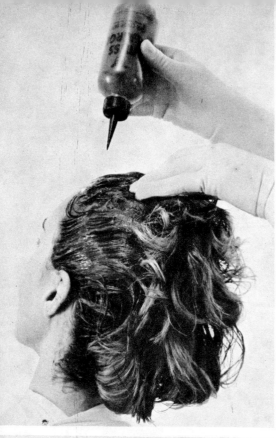

2. If ends are porous or damaged, apply the mixture to three-quarters of the strand only at this time.

3. Allow mixture to develop for about 15 minutes.

4. Strand Test for color development. Dry strand of hair and examine to see color development. When color has developed about halfway apply to ends. Note: If extremely damaged, dilute with a little shampoo before working through ends. Test frequently until desired shade has been reached and is even throughout. To cover gray completely, at least 20-30 minutes of developing time is necessary depending upon depth of color being used. The maximum development time for Miss Clairol is 45 minutes. Be sure to reapply Miss Clairol to the tested strand.

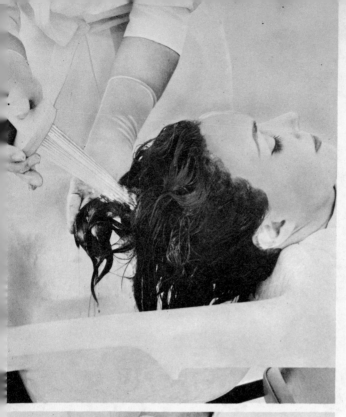

5. Rinse Miss Clairol thoroughly from hair with lukewarm water.

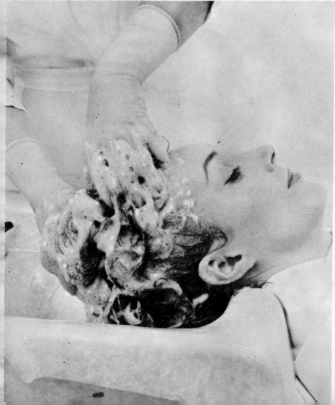

6. Shampoo with Clairol Green Shampoo for tinted hair.

METHOD B.

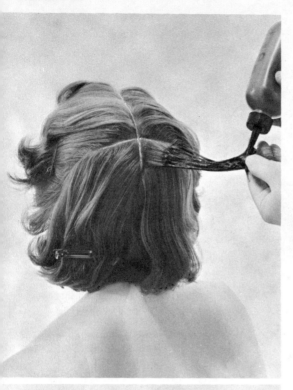

1. Part hair in 4 equal sections for tinting.

2. Apply Miss Clairol* beginning 1 inch away from scalp down to and including the ends. Use the applicator, brush or swab. Application is made 1 inch away from scalp because the hair away from the roots receives less natural body heat and will take a little longer to lighten.

3. Allow mixture to develop for 15 minutes.

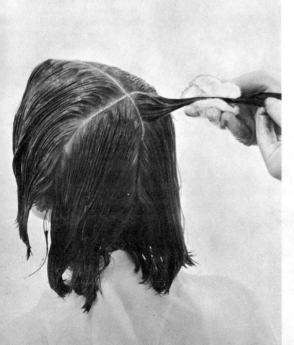

4. Strand Test until hair is lightened half as much as desired final result.

*If Preliminary Strand Test indicated that more than 15 minutes were required to lighten the shaft before application was made to roots, it is not advisable to make full color mixture. Leave some color for fresh mixture for root area application.

47

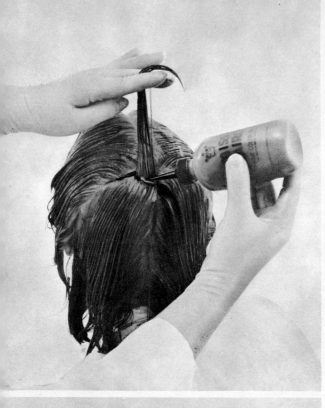

5. Apply Miss Clairol mixture to root area. Make certain that the hair is thoroughly saturated.

6. Leave tint on the hair until Strand Test shows an overall even shade has been reached.

7. Rinse hair with lukewarm water and shampoo with Clairol Green Shampoo.

How To Do a Miss Clairol Retouch Application

PRELIMINARY

1. Refer to Tint Record for the exact Miss Clairol color or formula used previously on your patron.

2. Do not shampoo hair unless hair is badly soiled or coated. Then dry thoroughly.

Application

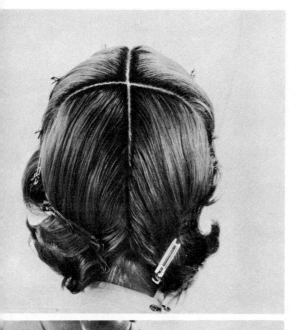

1. Part hair in 4 equal sections.

2. Outline with tint mixture.

49

3. Apply Miss Clairol liberally to new growth area only. Start tint application at back. Check back to make sure you have not missed any spots when you have finished your application. Reapply mixture to dry spots to keep retouch area moist. Avoid dripping on adjacent skin. Wipe away any dripping with water or soapy, absorbent cotton.

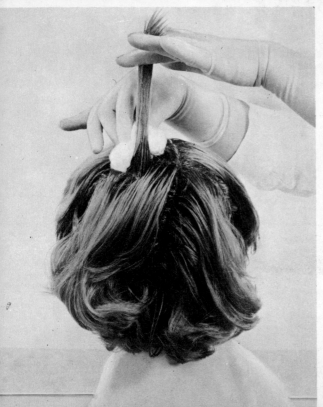

4. Strand Test root area frequently for color. Dry test strand and check color until desired shade is reached. Be sure to re-apply tint to dried strand after each test.

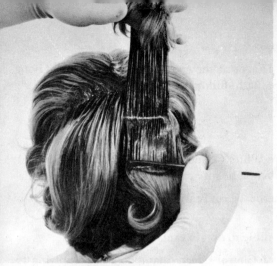

5. Comb Miss Clairol through hair if more color is needed on the shaft. Omit ends if they are porous.

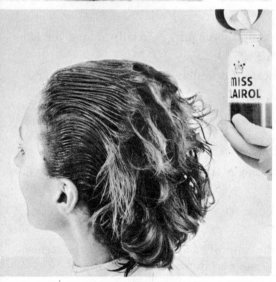

6. Dilute balance of tint mixture with Clairol Green Shampoo and pour through hair. Use equal parts shampoo to Miss Clairol mixture.

7. Pour mixture through hair and work it gently into a soap cap. Test immediately for color. If color is even, rinse thoroughly. If ends need additional color, allow mixture to develop a few minutes longer and test again until desired shade is reached.

8. Rinse thoroughly and shampoo with Clairol Green Shampoo.

51

Do's and Don't for Miss Clairol Creme Formula

Follow general Do's and Don't's at the end of Chapter 2. When giving a Miss Clairol Hair Color Bath, follow these as well.

Do's

1. Use Clairoxide or Pure White Creme Developer. Both are stable 20-volume peroxide. If you do not, be sure to use fresh 20-volume peroxide.

2. Apply thickly and generously, concentrating Miss Clairol where hair is most gray.

3. Apply as quickly as possible to obtain even development.

4. Dilute Miss Clairol with Clairol Green Shampoo when applying to porous ends.

5. Always rinse hair and scalp thoroughly, especially around the hairline, to remove all residual material.

6. Use Miss Clairol Applicator for neatest, fastest and best results.

7. Always wear rubber gloves during entire treatment.

Don't's

1. Don't shampoo before using Miss Clairol. Apply Miss Clairol to dry hair.

2. Don't apply to ends on a retouch unless you dilute with Clairol Green Shampoo.

3. Don't rub or massage the scalp when applying Miss Clairol. Remember it is a haircoloring and not a scalp treatment.

4. Don't apply Miss Clairol to ends until the color on the new growth is fully developed.

5. Don't pre-lighten unless a drastic color change is desired or unless hair needs corrective treatment.

6. Don't use Miss Clairol over metallic dyes, compound hennas or so-called color restorers. Discoloration or breakage may result.

7. Don't use Miss Clairol for coloring eyelashes or eyebrows.

8. Don't allow Miss Clairol to contact area in or around the eyes.

9. Don't save any Miss Clairol once it has been mixed with a developer or the container may burst. Use the amount you need, and discard the remaining mixture.

CHAPTER 4

MISS CLAIROL AS
A QUICK GLAMOUR
TREATMENT

FOR THE many women who are unhappy about dull or graying hair but timid about sudden change in haircoloring, Miss Clairol may be used effectively for a Quick Glamour Treatment. The formula is simple—1 part each of Miss Clairol Hair Color Bath, Clairoxide (or Pure White Creme Developer) and Clairol, the colorfast shampoo, Green for tint and lasting rinse users.

The treatment is quick. In 3 to 5 minutes, right at the shampoo basin, you can lighten the hair by a shade or two and bring out clear, glowing highlights. Though the change is subtle, the new beauty is a revelation. In most cases the Glamour Treatment serves as a reassuring introduction to the idea of permanent haircoloring.

SPECIAL USES FOR
MISS CLAIROL QUICK GLAMOUR TREATMENT
1. To give dancing highlights to dull hair.
2. As partial coverage on gray hair.
3. To brighten faded or sun-streaked hair.

Color Selection

All of the Miss Clairol colors may be used for the Glamour Treatment to match, to lighten or darken natural color with the exception of the three browns and black which are: Chestnut Brown, Coffee Brown and Sable Brown and Black Velvet.

How to Apply Miss Clairol as a Glamour
Treatment on Virgin Hair

PRELIMINARY

Be sure to give a Preliminary Patch Test before giving Glamour Treatment. (See page 11.)

1. Mix the formula: Combine 1 part Miss Clairol Hair Color Bath, plus 1 part Clairoxide (or Pure White Creme Developer), plus 1 part Clairol, the colorfast shampoo, Green for Tint and lasting rinse users— in plastic applicator or glass or plastic dish.

2. At shampoo basin, apply mixture quickly, evenly and liberally with applicator, swab or brush to the dry hair. Gently work into a lather. Do not rub into the scalp.

54

3. Allow to develop from 3 to 5 minutes. Make first strand color test at 3 minutes. When desired shade has been reached, rinse thoroughly with clear warm water.

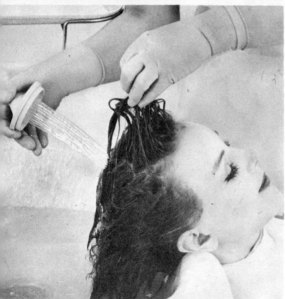

4. Shampoo with Clairol Green Shampoo.

Glamour Treatment Retouch

After two or three Glamour Treatments, use the retouch method of application for Miss Clairol. (See pages 49-51.)

Do's and Don't's for Glamour Treatment

Follow general Do's and Don't's at end of Chapter 2 as well as the following:

Do's

1. Mix Miss Clairol for a Glamour Treatment in plastic applicator or glass or plastic dish according to instructions.

2. Always use rubber gloves.

3. Apply as quickly as possible to obtain even development.

4. Use lighter shades for Glamour Treatment.

Don't's

1. Don't shampoo before giving Miss Clairol Glamour Treatment. Apply Miss Clairol to dry hair.

2. Don't rub or massage scalp when applying Miss Clairol.

3. Don't leave Miss Clairol when used as a Glamour Treatment on the hair too long if you wish only to add a little color.

4. Don't save any Miss Clairol once it has been mixed with developer. Use the amount you need, and discard the remaining mixture.

CHAPTER 5

CLAIROL SALON
FORMULA OIL
SHAMPOO TINT

CLAIROL SALON FORMULA is a permanent, penetrating haircoloring. In addition to natural-looking color it contains liquid shampoo to cleanse while it colors and fine conditioning oils. It has no lightening action.

Color Range

Salon Formula comes in a very wide range of colors to match or change natural hair colors. In the list below we have divided the colors into 2 groups according to their basic color tone to make selection easier.

SALON FORMULA COLORS

DRAB SERIES—NO RED OR GOLD

9A Towhead		**16**	Light Drab Brown
10B Sandy Blonde		**17**	Medium Drab Brown
15 Ash Blonde		**18**	Dark Drab Brown
15G Light Drab Blonde		**19**	Black
15E Dark Ash Blonde		**20**	Blue-Black

WARM SERIES—GOLD OR RED GOLD TONES

11A Light Blonde	**10D** Deep Golden Blonde
10A Golden Blonde	**15A** Medium Blonde

In addition to these colors there are Creme Toners for which hair must be pre-lightened. See Chapter 9—High Fashion Blonding with Clairol Creme Toner.

Color Selection for Salon Formula

The Salon Formula Chart shows the results obtained on 100% gray or white hair. Therefore the selection of color must take into consideration the percentage of gray and also the amount of natural red pigment in the patron's hair.

1. For 100% gray hair use the shade desired.

2. For 50% gray hair use a shade one shade lighter than final shade desired.

3. For 25% gray hair (or less) choose a shade two shades lighter than final shade.

4. If patron wants a shade lighter than her natural color and wants to cover her gray hair, pre-lightening is necessary.

5. If hair naturally contains a good deal of red, you may borrow from the Drab series to get the desired result.

THE 3 WAYS TO USE SALON FORMULA COLORS

It is important to remember that Salon Formula Shampoo Tint has no lightening action. Use it these 3 ways:

1. To match patron's natural color no pre-lightening is needed.

2. To make the hair lighter than the natural color, pre-lighten to a shade one or two shades lighter than the final color selected, to avoid the final result being darker than the shade desired. (See Chapter 7 on "Lightening.")

3. When hair is extremely resistant to color, pre-soften . . . apply lightener for just a few minutes so that little color change occurs.

How to Apply Salon Formula

1. Make Preliminary Patch or Skin Test for Hypersensitivity.

2. Make Preliminary Strand Test for Color Development.

3. Shampoo hair gently with Clairol, the colorfast shampoo, Green for Tint and lasting rinse users, pre-lightening if necessary. Rinse thoroughly.

4. Towel dry hair. This is advisable because it makes hair easier to handle and penetration is faster.

Mixing Salon Formula

Pour 1 bottle (¾ oz.) Clairol Salon Formula into a glass or plastic dish. Add an equal amount (¾ oz.) Clairoxide or Pure White Creme Developer.

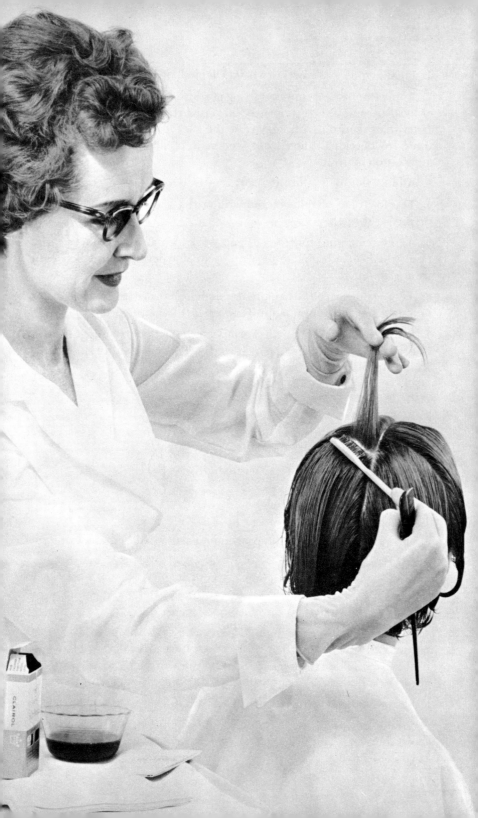

Application to Virgin Hair

1. Pre-shampoo and towel dry hair. Divide hair in 4 equal sections.

2. Apply tint to ¾ of strand, starting at scalp. Begin application at back of head because this section may be rinsed if the color has developed faster than the front. You may rinse the back area while the front continues to develop. When front section is predominantly gray, begin application in front.

3. Allow color to develop 10 to 20 minutes.

4. Test for color, washing strand with warm, soapy water and partially drying. Test often.

5. Apply remaining tint to ends and work into a soap cap over entire head when color begins to develop. Let color develop until it is even from scalp to ends.

6. Test again for color. If more development is needed, reapply color to test strand and continue until color has fully developed.

7. Rinse tint from hair with warm water. Shampoo thoroughly with Clairol, the colorfast shampoo, Green for Tint and lasting rinse users. Rub scalp as little as possible.

Application for Retouch
PRELIMINARY
1. Shampoo hair and towel dry. (Pre-lighten new growth if necessary before shampooing.)

2. Prepare tint mixture as for virgin hair.

Application

1. Section hair in 4 equal parts.

2. Begin application of tint by outlining partings. Start at back of head unless front is predominantly gray.

3. Apply tint to new growth only, making partings ¼ inch wide. Take care not to overlap from new growth to tinted hair. If this occurs, wipe off excess immediately to prevent line of demarcation.

4. Let color develop 5 minutes. Then, with towel or piece of cotton, partially dry tint at hairline and temples to retard color development in these areas more receptive to tint. Do not worry if you still see some gray hairs. Tint can be reapplied when blending through entire strand.

5. Strand Test for color frequently.

6. Comb the tint down the strand for an inch or two when Strand Test shows color almost fully developed. Blend to avoid a line of demarcation. If you observe dry spots, reapply tint to spots.

7. Dilute remaining tint with equal amount of Clairol, the colorfast shampoo, Green for Tint and lasting rinse users. Pour this mixture on ends first and work into a soap cap over entire head. If ends are damaged, tint should be diluted with a larger proportion of shampoo to avoid dark ends or streaks.

8. Allow mixture to remain on head, testing often for color until shade is evenly developed from scalp to ends.

9. Rinse hair and shampoo with Clairol Green Shampoo.

DEVELOPMENT TIME

Development time for Clairol Salon Formula Tint is from 20 to 45 minutes. Start strand-testing at 20 minutes. Color development ceases at 45 minutes.

Do's and Don't's for Salon Formula

Follow general Do's and Don't's at the end of Chapter 2. When using Salon Formula, follow these as well:

Do's

1. Always use Clairoxide, Pure White Creme Developer or fresh 20-volume peroxide.

2. Always pre-shampoo for best results.

3. Apply the tint as rapidly as possible for even results.

4. On porous or damaged ends make sure the balance of the tint is diluted sufficiently when blending through the ends.

5. Check the tint development much sooner at the temples and hairline.

6. For a shade lighter than natural always pre-lighten.

7. Keep merchandise at room temperature for best results.

Don't's

1. Don't comb through the shaft to blend the color until the color at the root is almost fully developed.

2. Don't apply on hair treated with metallic dyes, compound hennas or so-called color restorers. Discoloration or breakage may result.

3. Don't allow the lightener or tint to contact the area in or around the eyes.

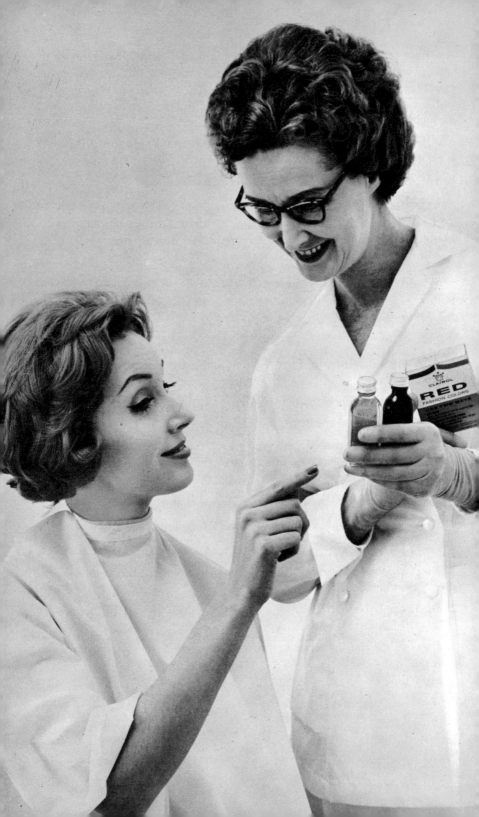

CHAPTER 6

RED
FASHION
COLORS

G REATLY in demand among a smart clientele are the bright, dramatic reds, achieved beautifully with an exciting Clairol category: Salon Formula Red Fashion Colors.

**Red
Fashion
Colors**

Each package of Red Fashion Color contains a bottle of red tint and one of Lady Clairol Whipped Creme Hair Lightener. The red tint can be used alone or combined for lightening action with the Lady Clairol.

The four thrilling Red Fashion Colors are:

1. Fire Silver—reddest and brightest

2. Sun Silver—glorious light golden red

3. Pink Silver—a stunning medium red

4. Cherry Silver—red, deep and dramatic

Each of the four Red Fashion Colors can be used these two ways:

1. **On natural (virgin) hair**—creates exciting red; lightens, too, when Lady Clairol is used.

2. **On pre-lightened hair**—an eye-catching red on moderately lightened hair . . . or a delicate pink-red tone on highly lightened hair.

SHADE SELECTOR—RED FASHION COLORS

SHADE NAME	ON NATURAL HAIR SHADE		ON HAIR PRE-LIGHTENED A FEW SHADES		ON PRE-LIGHTENED HAIR	
COLOR INTENSITY	The lighter the hair, the brighter the tone				ON HAIR HIGHLY PRE-LIGHTENED	
	FOR LIGHTER COLOR use the tint with Lady Clairol	FOR DEEPER COLOR use the tint without Lady Clairol	FOR LIGHT COLOR use the tint with Lady Clairol	FOR DEEPER COLOR use the tint without Lady Clairol	FOR LIGHT DELICATE TONE use the tint with Lady Clairol	FOR RED SHADES use the tint without Lady Clairol
FIRE SILVER the reddest and brightest	lightens and gives a bright red shade	gives red tone	gives a light bright orange red shade	gives the brightest red shade	gives a light delicate orange red tone	gives the brightest red shade
SUN SILVER a light golden red shade	lightens and gives a gold red shade	gives a gold red tone	gives a light gold red shade	gives a bright gold red shade	gives a light delicate golden red tone	gives a gold red shade
PINK SILVER a medium red shade	lightens and gives a medium red shade	gives a medium red tone	gives a light red shade	gives a brighter medium red shade	gives a light delicate pink red tone	gives a medium red shade
CHERRY SILVER a deep red shade	lightens and gives a deep red shade	gives a deep red tone	gives a medium red shade	gives a deep bright red shade	gives a light delicate red tone	gives a deep red shade

Want even more variety? Mix your own proportions.
Lighter shades—use more Lady Clairol and less red.
Darker shades—use less Lady Clairol and more red.

64

How to Apply Red Fashion Colors
PRELIMINARY

1. Select Red Fashion Color to be used.

2. Make a Patch Test 24 hours before application, (see page 11) using small portion of mixture of Red Fashion Color, Lady Clairol and Pure White Creme Developer you plan for final application.

3. Make a Preliminary Strand Test before proceeding with Red Fashion Color treatment. Mix a small portion of the mixture you plan to use: for example, ½ teaspoon Red Fashion Color, ½ teaspoon Lady Clairol, plus 2 teaspoons Pure White Creme Developer or Clairoxide. Apply to small strand following instructions for overall application. Note time required for proper color development and use as a guide. If hair is not accepting color evenly throughout, reconditioning treatments may be required before application of Red Fashion Color.

4. Examine the scalp to see that there are no cuts or abrasions. Do not apply Red Fashion Color or any other tint while they exist.

5. Have ready plastic applicator or glass or plastic dish. Never use a metal dish.

First Application on Virgin Hair for Exciting Red Color
MIXING DIRECTIONS

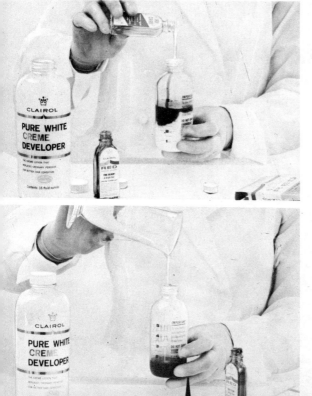

For lighter color:
Mix 1 bottle (¾ oz.) of Red Fashion Color and 1 bottle (¾ oz.) of Lady Clairol with 3 oz. Clairoxide or Pure White Creme Developer.

For deeper color and coverage on gray (50% or more):
Mix 1 bottle (¾ oz.) of Red Fashion Color with ¾ oz. Clairoxide or Pure White Creme Developer.

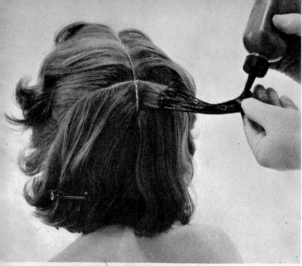

1. Part dry hair in 4 equal sections.

2. Start 1 inch from roots and apply mixture down hair shaft.

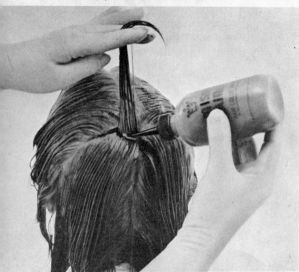

3. When hair has lightened half as much as the final color desired, apply mixture to root area.

4. Make a Strand Test to check whether color is even throughout and has developed enough.

5. When color is even from scalp to ends, rinse and shampoo.

Retouch Application

1. Part hair in equal sections and apply mixture to regrowth area. Allow it to develop until Strand Test shows roots have reached the desired shade.

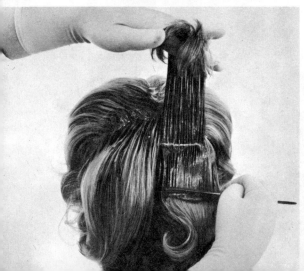

2. Now start combing balance of mixture through ¾ of strand if ends hold color well. If not, comb through entire strand.

3. Test for color. When color is even, rinse and shampoo.

67

Shaft not holding color? If during retouch this problem exists, follow this method:

1. Part hair in 4 equal sections. Apply mixture to regrowth area. Allow it to develop until roots have reached the desired shade.

2. Use an equal amount of Red Fashion Color and developer as a soap cap over the entire head.

3. Test for color. When color is even, rinse and shampoo.

First Application to Hair Pre-Lightened a Few Shades

Pre-lighten hair using Lady Clairol Instant Whip or Lady Clairol Whipped Creme Hair Lightener. Hair should be lightened one or two shades lighter than final Red Fashion Color selected. Then shampoo, rinse and towel dry.

MIXING DIRECTIONS

For lighter color:

Mix 1 bottle (¾ oz.) Red Fashion Color and 1 bottle (¾ oz.) Lady Clairol with 3 oz. Clairoxide or Pure White Creme Developer.

For deeper color:

Mix 1 bottle (¾ oz.) Red Fashion Color and ¾ oz. Clairoxide or Pure White Creme Developer.

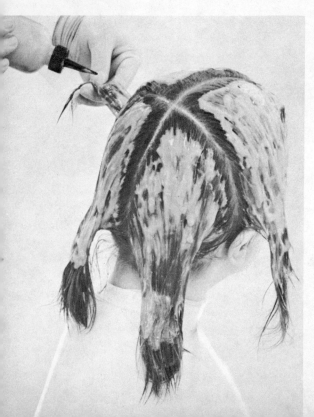

1. Part hair in 4 equal sections. Apply color mixture ½ inch away from scalp down ¾ of strand, omitting ends.

2. Now **return to root** area and **apply color.**

3. Start taking Strand Tests for color after 5 minutes of development.

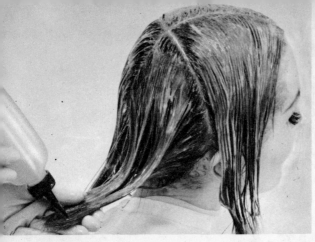

4. Work balance of mixture through the ends as soon as color has begun to develop.

5. Test again. When color is even from scalp to ends, rinse and shampoo.

Retouch on Hair Pre-Lightened a Few Shades

1. Pre-lighten regrowth area only. Shampoo, rinse and towel-dry.

2. Apply mixture to lightened regrowth area and allow color to develop until Strand Test shows enough color at roots. If left on too long, newly lightened area may become too bright in color.

3. Blend by combing through ¾ of shaft.

4. Work balance through ends like a soap cap.

5. Test for color. When even throughout, rinse and shampoo.

70

First Application on Highly Pre-Lightened Hair

Pre-lighten hair using Ultra-Blue Lady Clairol Cremogenized Hair Lightener with 2 Protinator Envelopes. Hair must be lightened only to the gold stage for the red shades. For "pink-red" tones, lighten hair to the yellow or pale yellow stage. Shampoo, rinse and towel dry.

MIXING DIRECTIONS

For delicate tones:

Mix 1 bottle (¾ oz.) Red Fashion Color and 1 bottle (¾ oz.) Lady Clairol with 3 oz. Clairoxide or Pure White Creme Developer.

For red shades:

Mix 1 bottle (¾ oz.) Red Fashion Color and ¾ oz. Clairoxide or Pure White Creme Developer.

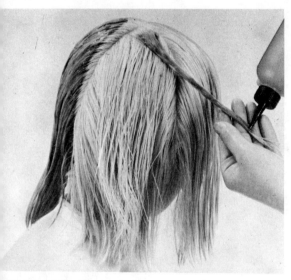

1. Part highly pre-lightened hair in 4 equal portions. Apply mixture to back portion first. Start ½ inch from roots and apply down to ends of hair shaft. Be sure that ends are thoroughly saturated with mixture.

2. Allow tint to develop for a few minutes. Keep testing until the ends begin to hold color.

71

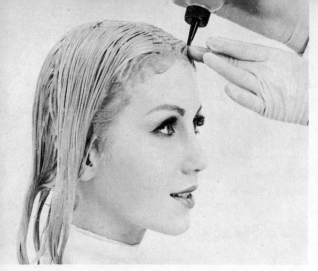

3. Apply to root area when tests show color on ends deep enough. However, if shaft and ends throw off color before root application, dilute remaining mixture by adding an equal amount of Clairoxide or Pure White Creme Developer. (This will prevent roots being redder or deeper than ends.)

4. Pour enough of the mixture through the entire head to blend color. Comb through hair until color is even from scalp to ends.

5. Test frequently. The longer the Red Color develops, the deeper the final color will be.

6. When hair has reached the color desired, add equal amount of Clairol, the colorfast shampoo, Blue for Lightened and Toned Hair, to whatever amount remains in the applicator.

72

7. Work gently into a soap cap. If no tint remains, apply shampoo directly to hair to make a soap cap.

8. Rinse thoroughly. No after-shampoo is required. (However, if you want to lighten shade a bit, you may give a light shampoo.)

Retouch for Highly Lightened Hair

1. Pre-lighten hair on new growth only.
2. After pre-lightening, apply color mixture the same way as for first application on highly lightened hair.

To Change from a Blonde to Red Shade

If your customer wishes to change from a blonde to a redhead, the formula to use is:

¾ oz. Red Fashion Color

¾ oz. Clairoxide or Pure White Creme Developer
    After pre-lightening the new growth, apply as you would a Red Fashion Toner.

    On the next application you can avoid pre-lightening by using the regular formula:

¾ oz. Red Fashion Color

¾ oz. Lady Clairol

3 oz. Clairoxide or Pure White Creme Developer
    Use this formula on all future applications.

Tips on Using Red Fashion Colors

1. When ends are a problem and do not hold color, start application from ends up whether you are doing an application on the natural hair shade or on a retouch.

2. When the hair shaft appears to be faded and lacks color even after a color treatment, it is time to start decreasing the Lady Clairol in the mixture. If the problem is serious, omit the Lady Clairol completely for faded areas or use Clair-Fill.

3. If you wish to lighten color even further, you can increase the amount of the developer to dilute the color even further.

Do's and Don't's for Red Fashion Colors

Follow general Do's and Don't's at the end of Chapter 2. When using Red Fashion Colors, follow these as well.

Do's

1. Always keep partly used bottles tightly closed.

2. Be sure Red Fashion Colors and developer are at room temperature.

3. For best results use Clairoxide or Pure White Creme Developer. Both are superior, stabilized 20-volume hydrogen peroxide.

4. Be sure to use a good bland shampoo that does not strip color from hair. Clairol, the colorfast shampoo, Blue for Lightened and Toned Hair, is ideal for this purpose.

Don't's

1. Don't keep any mixture after Lady. Clairol or developer has been added.

2. Don't use Clairol Red Fashion Colors or any permanent coloring as an eyelash or eyebrow dye.

CHAPTER 7

CLAIROL
LIGHTENERS AND
WHAT THEY DO

LIGHTENING the hair color, or blonding, is one of the most important and glamorizing services the beauty salon has to offer. Clairol prefers to use the professional term *lighteners* rather than *bleaches* for its fine products designed to remove pigment from the hair. You'll find using the term "lightener" to your patrons has a softer, more pleasing connotation than the harsher term "bleach".

Clairol lighteners may be used for two purposes:

1. *As a color treatment* to lighten the hair to the final shade desired.

2. *As a preliminary treatment* to prepare the hair for the application of a tint or Clairol Creme Toner.

If the patron desires a drastic change to a much lighter than natural shade, the lightener must be used to remove pigment before a tint is applied. For instance, a lightener is always necessary before applying one of the delicate Clairol Creme Toner shades.

Effects of Lightening

As hair is lightened, it goes through a succession of 7 color changes to change from black to pale yellow.

Stage 1—Black hair changes to

Stage 2—Brown, then to

Stage 3—Red, next to

Stage 4—Red-gold, then to

Stage 5—Gold, then to

Stage 6—Yellow, and finally to

Stage 7—Pale yellow (almost white)

The hair also becomes more porous during lightening, a necessary condition to permit penetration of a Clairol Creme Toner. Even naturally light hair must go through the lightening process to lighten and achieve the necessary degree of porosity.

1
black

2
brown

3
red

4
red-gold

5
gold

6
yellow

7
pale yellow

THE 7 STAGES IN LIGHTENING FROM BLACK TO THE PALE YELLOW (ALMOST WHITE) STAGE

A natural head of black hair will go through seven stages before it reaches the Pale Yellow (almost white) Stage. The degree hair lightens depends upon the amount of time the lightener is left on and lightener chosen. Note how red tones are eliminated as final stages of lightening are reached.

TIMING CHART FOR 7 STAGES OF LIGHTENING

CLAIROLITE	*45 minutes*	
LADY CLAIROL	*45 minutes*	
ULTRA-BLUE + 1 PROTINATOR	*2 hours*	
LADY CLAIROL + 2 BOOSTERS	*2 hours*	
ULTRA-BLUE + 2 PROTINATORS	*2 hours*	
BLUE LIGHTENING	*1½ hours*	
ULTRA-BLUE + 3 PROTINATORS	*2 hours*	

1	**2**	**3**	**4**	**5**	**6**	**7**
black	brown	red	red-gold	gold	yellow	pale yellow

This timing chart applies to retouch at roots only. For application on shaft of virgin hair, use double the amount of timing.

77

	LADY CLAIROL WHIPPED CREME	INSTANT WHIP LADY CLAIROL	ULTRA-BLUE LADY CLAIROL
PREPARATION	Whip	Stir or Shake	Stir or Shake
APPLICATION	Brush	Brush or Applicator	Brush or Applicator
LIGHTENING ACTION Without Booster or Protinator	Faster and greater than oil lighteners, to be used on hair not too difficult to lighten.	A little faster and greater than Lady Clairol Whipped Creme—to be used on hair not too difficult to lighten.	Mild and gentle, comparable to an oil lightener—should be confined to highlighting, brightening or lightening non-resistant hair only a few shades.
LIGHTENING ACTION With 1 Booster (1 Protinator with Ultra-Blue)	Increases the lightening action and speed so that light hair and non-resistant hair can be pre-lightened for the light toner colors.	A little faster and greater than Lady Clairol Whipped Creme.	Faster and greater than either Lady Clairol Whipped Creme or Instant Whip.
LIGHTENING ACTION With 2 Boosters (2 Protinators with Ultra-Blue)	Increases speed and lightening action to maximum needed for high fashion blonde shades, decolorizing a tint.	A little faster and greater than Lady Clairol Whipped Creme.	A little faster and greater than Instant Whip. The most comfortable for high fashion blonding.

Selection of the Proper Lightener
CLAIROL FAMILY OF LIGHTENERS

Clairol has developed a scientifically formulated lightener for every lightening need. Each is designed to make your work easier and faster . . . to give your patrons new comfort and beautiful, reliable results. There are three creme lighteners in the Lady Clairol group:

Ultra-Blue Lady Clairol Cremogenized Hair Lightener —with Protinator Envelopes

This product lightens *lighter* and *more quickly* than any product on the market. Can be used to any degree of lightening desired. Best for lightening prior to application of high fashion Clairol Creme Toner shades. Here are the exclusive advantages of Ultra-Blue Lady Clairol which have made it the new standard of superiority in lightening:

1. Greater comfort than ever before during lightening and toning.

2. Lighter, faster results.

3. Double drabbing action.

4. Refined Protinator dissolves quickly and completely, will not block applicator nozzle.

5. Uniform consistency and performance—mixture never varies from bottle to bottle; always produces a smooth, thick creme.

6. No running, dripping or drying out regardless of the number of Protinator envelopes used.

7. Lightener washes out quickly and easily.

Ultra-Blue Lady Clairol Protinator, unlike any other product used in conjunction with lighteners, is formulated to condition the protein structure of the hair as well as increase the lightening and drabbing ability of Ultra-Blue.

Protinator was especially formulated for use with Ultra-Blue. Mixed with it, it makes the action of Ultra-Blue more effective in every way. It cannot be used effectively with any other hair lightener.

WHO SHOULD USE ULTRA-BLUE?

Generally anyone can use Ultra-Blue Lady Clairol. The degree and speed of lightening can be controlled to assure results desired.

1. The Clairol Creme Toner user who wants quick and lightest lightening uses: Ultra-Blue with 2 Protinator envelopes. To mix: Add 2 Protinator envelopes to 4 oz. Clairoxide; then add 2 oz. Ultra-Blue.

2. The patron who wants moderate lightening (*i.e., she is not using a Clairol Creme Toner*) **or the naturally light-haired woman who may or may not be using a Clairol Creme Toner uses:** Ultra-Blue with 1 Protinator. To mix: Add 1 Protinator to 4 oz. Clairoxide; then add 2 oz. Ultra-Blue.

3. The patron who wants to lighten her hair color slightly (*recommended for natural light shade of hair*) **uses:** Ultra-Blue with no Protinator: To mix: Add 2 oz. Ultra-Blue to 4 oz. Clairoxide.

How to Mix Ultra-Blue Lady Clairol Hair Lightener and Ultra-Blue Lady Clairol Protinator

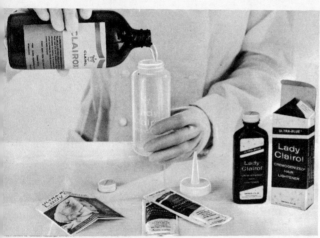

1. Pour 4 oz. Clairoxide into applicator.

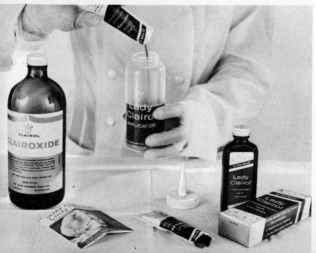

2. When Ultra-Blue Protinator is to be used for added speed and lightening action, make sure it is finely powdered by squeezing the envelope.

3. Then pour the Ultra-Blue Protinator into the applicator.

80

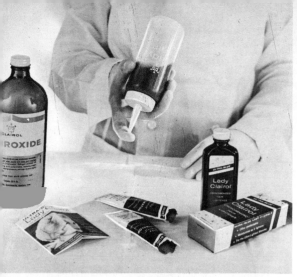

4. Cover top and shake twice.

5. Add 2 oz. Ultra-Blue Lady Clairol.

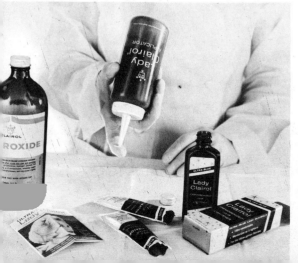

6. Now shake vigorously for 20 seconds. Combine in same order when Protinator is not used. When using bowl and brush, combine ingredients in same order; then stir for 30 seconds or until mixture is thick and creamy.

81

**Instant Whip
Lady Clairol
Hair Lightener**

For the patron who wants *medium* lightening results. Comes in creme form. Quicker than Whipped Cream but not as quick as Ultra-Blue with 2 Protinators. Conditions as it lightens.

**Lady Clairol
Whipped Creme
Hair Lightener**

For the patron who wants *gradual* lightening. A thick creme, Whipped Creme must be whipped with stainless steel or nickel beater in glass or plastic bowl. It is applied with a brush.

WHO SHOULD USE INSTANT WHIP OR WHIPPED CREME LADY CLAIROL?

1. **The Miss Clairol user who wants to lighten her Miss Clairol shade slightly.** To mix: 2 or 3 capfuls with Miss Clairol will do the trick.

2. **The patron who wants moderate lightening** (*i.e., she does not use a hair color or has naturally light hair*) uses: No Lady Clairol Lightening booster. To mix: 4 oz. Pure White or Clairoxide and either 2 oz. Instant Whip or Whipped Creme.

3. The patron who wants moderate lightening *(i.e., she does not use a Clairol Creme Toner)* uses: 1 Booster with Instant Whip or Whipped Creme. To mix: Add 1 Booster to 4 oz. Pure White or Clairoxide; then add 2 oz. either Instant Whip or Whipped Creme.

4. The patron who lightens for a Clairol Creme Toner uses: 2 Boosters with Instant Whip or Whipped Creme. To mix: Add 2 Boosters to 4 oz. Pure White or Clairoxide; then add 2 oz. either Instant Whip or Whipped Creme.

NOTE: Lady Clairol Lightening Boosters are not lighteners. They cannot be used alone. They should always be mixed with Instant Whip or Whipped Creme Lady Clairol.

How to Mix Instant Whip Lady Clairol Creme Lightener

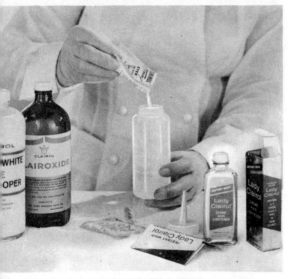

1. Pour 4 oz. of Clairoxide or Pure White Creme Developer into applicator bottle. If Lightening Booster is to be added for increased speed and lightening action, make sure it is finely powdered by crushing envelope with fingers. Then tear the top off the envelope evenly. Using the envelope as a funnel, insert it a little way into the neck of the applicator and let powder flow inside. Cover top; with finger on top, shake once or twice. Pour in entire 2 oz. bottle of Instant Whip. Cover top; with finger on top, shake up and down vigorously for about 20 seconds. Mixture is thick and creamy.

2. When a bowl is used instead of applicator, combine ingredients in same order; then stir with brush or swab stick for 30 seconds or until mixture is thick and creamy.

83

How to Mix Lady Clairol Whipped Creme Hair Lightener

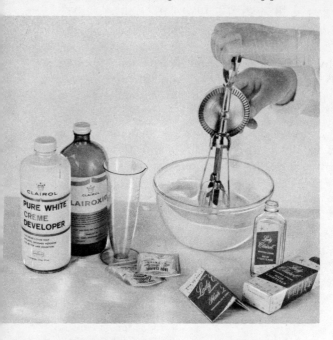

Mix 2 oz. Lady Clairol, 4 oz. Clairoxide or Pure White Creme Developer in glass or plastic bowl, and add Lightening Booster if increased speed and lightening action is desired. Whip to desired cream consistency using stainless-steel beater.

Lady Clairol Lightening Booster

One or two envelopes of Lightening Booster are added to Lady Clairol or Instant Whip whenever either is used to prelighten hair for toning. Lightning Booster increases the speed and the lightening action of both. It is never used with Ultra-Blue Lady Clairol.

Other Specialized Lighteners

Clairolite

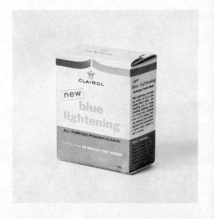

Clairol Blue Lightening

Clairolite

Clairolite is a mild oil lightener used to lighten and brighten hair in a simple one-step treatment. Four of the shades add temporary color highlights as they lighten. These colors are certified and may be used without a patch test. Those allergic to tints may use them. *Neutral* adds no color and so is frequently used to pre-soften hair for tint application. Colors and the results they produce are listed below:

Gold No. 1—lightens and adds gold highlights.

Silver No. 2—lightens and adds ash highlights that minimize unwanted red and gold tones.

Red No. 3—lightens and adds red highlights.

Neutral No. 4—contains no color, simply lightens.

Sparkling Silver No. 5—minimizes unwanted red and gold tones.

Clairol Blue Lightening

Clairol Blue Lightening is an all-purpose lightener in powder form. It contains Blue-Lite, an exclusive Clairol ingredient, which gives it greater speed, lightening and drabbing action than other powder lighteners. Blue Lightening is used whenever extensive lightening is required and hair is strong and in good condition. For example: frosting; tipping; streaking; pre-lightening extremely resistant, strong dark hair for toning; and stripping tint to make a change to a lighter shade.

How to Mix Clairolite

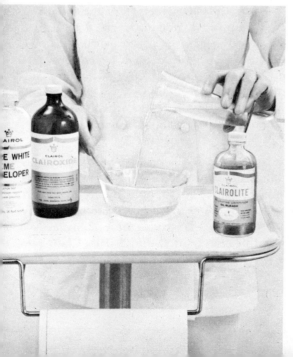

Mix 1 part Clairolite with 2 parts Clairoxide or Pure White Creme Developer in a glass or plastic dish to lighten and brighten as a complete coloring treatment. Use diluted mixture to pre-soften: 1 part Clairolite to 3-4 parts developer.

How to Mix Blue Lightening Powder

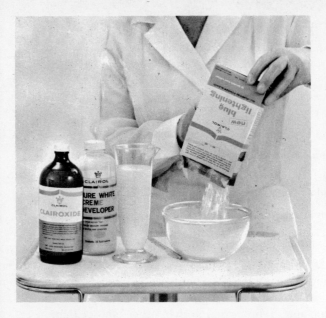

Empty contents of package into glass or plastic bowl. Use one package for the average retouch. For virgin hair additional amounts may be needed. Add from 7 to 8 oz. of Clairoxide or 8 to 9 oz. of Pure White Creme Developer; stir to make a smooth, creamy paste. If the mixture seems heavy, add from ¼ to ½ oz. more developer.

Lightening as a Coloring Treatment

Removing pigment from the hair by the lightening process is a method of obtaining a *new color*. As the pigment is removed, the hair goes through the following color stages as it lightens:

Black to **Brown** / **Brown** to **Red** / **Red** to **Red-Gold** / **Red-Gold** to **Gold** / **Gold** to **Yellow** / **Yellow** to **Pale Yellow** (almost white) /

To LIGHTEN as a coloring treatment, use any of the following:
1. Ultra-Blue without Protinator will highlight, brighten or lighten non-resistant hair a few shades. Use glass or plastic bowl. Mix 1 oz. Ultra-Blue with 2 oz. Clairoxide or Pure White Creme Developer. Make Preliminary Strand Test using small quantity of mixture, and check exact timing necessary (usually 1-2 min.). Then proceed with full treatment. Work mixture through hair as you would a shampoo. Wait time indicated by previous test. Rinse and shampoo immediately. Treatment is complete.

2. Add Clairolite Neutral No. 4 or Lady Clairol Instant Whip to Miss Clairol. As little as 2 capfuls of Lady Clairol Instant Whip can be added for a slight increase in lightening action, using the regular 1 part Clairoxide to 1 part Miss Clairol. However, when you use ¼ oz. Lady Clairol or more, you must use more Clairoxide—the proportion is 1 part Clairoxide for each part of Miss Clairol, plus 2 parts Clairoxide for each part Lady Clairol.

HOW TO USE ANY LADY CLAIROL WHEN BRIGHTENING AND HIGHLIGHTING TO MAKE ONLY A SLIGHT CHANGE:

Use glass or plastic bowl. Mix 1 ounce Lady Clairol with 4 ounces Clairoxide or Pure White Creme Developer. Since Lady Clairol lightens quite rapidly, make Preliminary Strand Test. For this purpose, use small amount of mixture just prepared. Check exact timing necessary to reach desired shade (usually 1-2 min.). Then proceed with full treatment: Work mixture throughout hair as you would a shampoo. Wait time indicated by previous test. Rinse and shampoo immediately. Treatment is complete.

Drabbing with Silver Drops During Lightening

Silver Drops, an exclusive Clairol product, drabs lightened and tinted hair and helps eliminate unwanted gold or red tones. Silver Drops is a concentrated color. The lighter the hair, the less Silver Drops is required.

Use Silver Drops with Lady Clairol Whipped Creme Hair Lightener or Instant Whip (no Boosters in mixture) or with Neutral Clairolite.

Do not use Silver Drops with Ultra-Blue or Blue Lightening. Both contain special drabbers in their formulas.

HOW TO USE SILVER DROPS WHEN LIGHTENING

	WITH 2 OZ. WHIPPED CREME OR INSTANT WHIP LADY CLAIROL MIXTURE	WITH 1 OZ. NEUTRAL CLAIROLITE MIXTURE
TO DRAB BLONDE HAIR	Add 5 to 10 Silver Drops	Add 2 to 5 Silver Drops
TO DRAB LIGHT BROWN HAIR	Add 10 to 15 Silver Drops	Add 2 to 10 Silver Drops
TO DRAB DARK BROWN OR BLACK HAIR	Add 15 to 20 Silver Drops	Add 4 to 12 Silver Drops

You may vary the number of Silver Drops to fit individual cases. However, never use more than 25 Silver Drops. A Preliminary Patch Test is necessary when Silver Drops is added to any formula.

Application of Lightener
PRE-TESTING
1. Make a Patch Test if you plan to use a Creme Toner, at least 24 hours before toning. (See page 11.) Use the Creme Toner shade you have selected for the treatment.

2. Make Preliminary Strand Test. This is necessary to predetermine the length of time to leave any Lady Clairol lightening mixture on the hair and to check whether hair is in suitable condition for lightening. To save your patron time, when the Patch Test is made, cut off several full strands of hair. Secure them with tape and use for the following Preliminary Strand Test:

Combine one of the following mixtures in a glass or plastic bowl:
2 tsp. Clairoxide or Pure White Creme Developer with
either
1 tsp. Lady Clairol, plus ¼ tsp. Lightening Booster
or
1 tsp. Ultra-Blue, plus ½ tsp. Protinator

(These proportions are equivalent to mixture used in the final lightening process.)

Apply this mixture to a full strand of hair. Wait 45 minutes, then dry strand and check for color. If it has not been reached, reapply mixture and repeat test frequently until desired shade is achieved. Rinse immediately and dry. Record the time it has taken to lighten the strand and use it to gauge approximate time the full treatment will require.

WHAT TO LOOK FOR DURING THE STRAND TEST:

1. If, after the first color check, hair is not light enough, mixture must be reapplied and left on for a longer time.

2. If hair is too light after the first color check, mixture must be left on for a shorter time or a milder formula considered, depending on hair condition.

3. If hair is extremely strong and resistant and if Strand Test indicated that greater speed and lightening action would be needed to reach shade required for Creme Toner selected, you should plan to use Ultra-Blue Lady Clairol and 3 envelopes of Protinator for full treatment, strand-testing first.

4. If Strand Test shows that reduced lightening will be sufficient, one Lightening Booster (one Protinator with Ultra-Blue) may be used in full treatment. Strand Test new mixture to check timing.

5. If hair is very dark, it may not lighten sufficiently in one application, in which case additional treatments may be necessary. If a second is required, it is good policy to allow a day or two to elapse between treatments.

6. If hair has been damaged, the Strand Test must be carefully observed for any indication of breakage or discoloration. If this happens, do not proceed with the treatment without first reconditioning and retesting. If the desired color is achieved and no breakage occurs, you may proceed with full treatment.

Before proceeding with pre-lightening for Creme Toner, do two things:

1. Make a careful examination of patron's scalp to see that there are no abrasions, eruptions or open wounds. Do not proceed if any of these conditions exists.

2. Make a *fresh* mixture of the lightening formula decided upon, according to product directions on pages 80 and 83.

Application of Lighteners to Virgin Hair

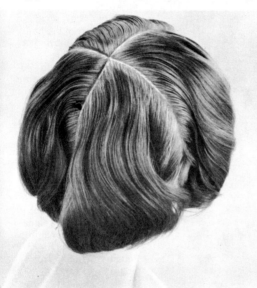

1. Part hair in 4 sections using applicator or rat-tail comb.

2. Make ¼-inch partings at the darkest part of hair (usually the back of the head). Starting 1 inch away from scalp, apply mixture generously to each strand. Continue ¼-inch partings and application until all 4 quarters are covered. If ends are porous or in a weakened condition, omit and apply a little later. You may protect scalp at root area with strips of rolled cotton to prevent lightener from getting to scalp when hair strands are saturated with the lightener.

3. Begin strand-testing for color on 1-inch strand from first quarter completed. If test shows hair has not been lightened enough, reapply mixture to strand and continue testing frequently, until test shows hair is half way lightened. Wipe off excess lightener with damp towel.

4. Apply lightener to root area. Starting at the darkest part of the head, make ⅛-inch partings and apply mixture thickly to the 1-inch area formerly uncovered by the lightener.

5. Gently work remaining mixture in applicator throughout the hair when application of root area is complete. Pile hair on top of head. Do not rub lightening mixture into the scalp.

6. Strand Test. About 10 minutes before Preliminary Strand Test indicated necessary, dry a full strand of hair from scalp to end and check for lightness and evenness of color. If hair is not light enough, reapply mixture to strand and continue testing frequently.

7. When desired shade is reached (gold, yellow or pale yellow if a Creme Toner is to be applied), rinse and shampoo immediately. Hair is ready for setting. If a Creme Toner application is to be made, it should be applied immediately after the shampoo.

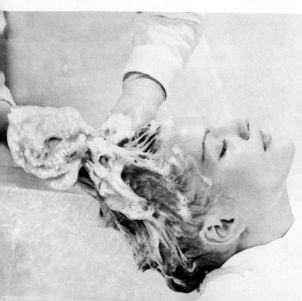

NOTE: Lightening on very dark hair. The shaft of the hair lightens slower than the root area. With very dark hair, *two* applications of the lightener are always necessary to reach the pale yellow (decolorized) stage.

This application may be done the same day if the hair is in strong, healthy condition. If not, it may be made within 24 hours of the original application. If the second application is to be made on the same day, it is better not to shampoo the first application out.

It is better merely to wipe off some of the original application and reapply a fresh mixture to the shaft area. If this method is followed, you are able to do two applications on the shaft and one on the root (providing hair is in good condition). Apply lightening mixture at the root sometime during the second application of the lightener.

NOTE: Hint for hairdressers who use brush instead of applicator and prefer to work slowly: Mix only half the required quantity of lightening mixture. Apply to the back of the head. Then mix the other half and apply to remaining portion of the head. This will give fresh, quick lightening action for the entire head.

Retouch Application

1. Divide hair in 4 sections, then make ⅛-inch partings using rat-tail comb or applicator.
2. Apply lightener generously to new growth. Do not overlap into hair previously lightened.

3. After first 15-20 minutes, dry 1-inch strand and test for color. If it has not been reached, reapply mixture and continue testing frequently.
4. When desired shade is reached, rinse and shampoo immediately. Hair is ready for setting or application of Clairol Creme Toner.

91

Do's and Don't's for Lightening

Follow the general Do's and Don't's at the end of Chapter 2. When lightening, follow these as well.

Do's

1. Always use Clairoxide, Pure White Creme Developer or any fresh 20-volume hydrogen peroxide.
2. Make a Preliminary Strand Test to determine proper timing and condition of the hair.
3. Wear rubber gloves during the entire treatment.
4. Use Lightening Booster only with Lady Clairol Whipped Creme Hair Lightener or Instant Whip. Use Protinator only with Ultra-Blue.
5. Use Clairol, the colorfast shampoo, Blue for Lightened and Toned Hair.

Don't's

1. Don't prepare, mix or store Blue Lightening mixture in a closed container because it may burst.

2. Don't apply lightener to hair coated with metallic dyes, compound hennas or restorers without first reconditioning the hair to remove such substances. Re-test for these substances before lightener is applied. (See 1-20 test, page 197.)

3. Don't let the lightener contact area around the eyes.

4. Don't use lightener if the scalp has open cuts or abrasions.

5. Don't use Protinator with any lightener other than Ultra-Blue Lady Clairol.

6. Don't brush or pre-shampoo before using lightener.

7. Don't mix Ultra-Blue with Miss Clairol, Instant Whip or Whipped Creme.

8. Don't mix Silver Drops or any other product designed to remove red or gold tones with Ultra-Blue.

CHAPTER 8

LIGHTENING FOR CLAIROL CREME TONER HIGH-FASHION BLONDE SHADES

THE current style importance of the new high-fashion blonde shades, so beautifully achieved with Clairol Creme Toner, gives the hair-colorist an opportunity to display the finest expression of her art, as well as to win new glory and profit for her salon.

Success in creating these subtle pale gold, silver, ash, platinum, chiffon, pearl and champagne shades is entirely dependent on proper pre-lightening. So important is this preliminary lightening step that we give you this special chapter on lightening the hair before applying the Clairol Creme Toner shade selected. Hair must always be made not only *light* enough but *porous* enough to be receptive to the Creme Toner. Clairol uses the name Creme Toner for its exclusive high-fashion blonde tints and *toning* for the coloring process of achieving them.

The Two Basic Steps for Creme Toner Blonding

Step 1. Pre-lightening is always necessary, carried to the correct stage required for the Creme Toner selected. Hair, according to its original color, must go through successive changes in color during the lightening process. (See chart, page 76.) To reach the right stage for the Creme Toner tints the hair must be lightened to the correct pale shade among the three lightest in the lightening spectrum: gold, yellow or pale yellow.

In the case of naturally blonde hair the lightening must be continued for the full time needed for the hair to reach the proper degree of porosity (45 minutes minimum) even though the required color stage is reached sooner.

Step 2. Application of the Clairol Creme Toner to the correctly pre-lightened hair is made to obtain the glamorous high-fashion blonde tint desired.

PRE-LIGHTENING FOR CREME TONER DOES 2 THINGS

1. It lightens hair to a stage that is pale enough to receive the delicate Creme Toner color.

2. It makes the hair porous enough to absorb the color.

If hair is not sufficiently porous, it will throw off the Creme Toner color.

During the lightening process it is important to make two tests... for color and for porosity.

HOW TO MAKE COLOR TEST

To determine if the hair is lightened to the stage required for the Creme Toner shade decided upon, simply wash the lightener off a single strand and examine the color. If "underdone," reapply lightener to strand, continue lightening and test again. Hair should be lightened *only* as far as the shade advised.

When hair has lightened to the desired pre-tinting shade, test for porosity.

HOW TO CHECK FOR POROSITY

It is very difficult to judge porosity unless certain basic questions are answered:

1. What is the final shade desired?

2. What is the natural hair color?

3. What is the hair texture?

4. How long has the hair already been lightened?

Time Element

If lightener has been on hair for *several hours,* chances are it is porous enough and ready to accept the Creme Toner color.

ONLY SURE WAY OF DETERMINING POROSITY

If there is any doubt about the proper porosity, take a Strand Test and examine strand.

1. When the shade produced matches the shade on the color chart that means porosity is sufficient.

2. Color not deep enough or drab enough (too much gold color coming through) means hair is not porous enough and must be lightened further.

3. Color too drab, too gray or not holding color means hair has become over-porous.

4. No color-take means the porosity of the hair is far from ready and requires much longer lightening.

HOW TO STRAND TEST FOR COLOR TO DETERMINE POROSITY

When you think the lightener is almost ready (15 to 20 minutes away from the final desired result), wash the lightener from a single strand of hair, towel dry and apply the desired toner color. Use a small amount mixed according to directions.)

Let it develop 15 to 20 minutes. Rinse and dry. From this result you can determine if hair is lightened to the proper stage and whether it has the required amount of porosity.

POINTS TO REMEMBER ABOUT PRE-LIGHTENING BLONDE AND GRAY HAIR

All hair must reach the correct degree of *porosity* as well as color in pre-lightening for a high-fashion Creme Toner. In the case of blonde, gray or white hair it frequently takes less time to lighten than to achieve the porosity needed. The lightener should remain on the hair not less than 45 minutes and up to 2 hours on coarse or resistant hair.

On light shades lightening will take at least 45 minutes. The darker the hair, the longer the lightening period. Do not lighten beyond the lightening stage needed for the Creme Toner color selected.

THE 7 STAGES OF LIGHTENING

Hair must go through many stages of color as it lightens. For instance, a natural head of black hair being lightened for toning with a silver or platinum Creme Toner must go from black to brown, to red, to red-gold, to gold, to yellow and finally to pale yellow (almost white). So delicate are the high-fashion blonde shades that pre-lightening is necessary to the correct color among the last three stages of lightening—gold, yellow or pale yellow. (See next chapter, page 102, for table showing correct lightening stage required for Creme Toner selected.)

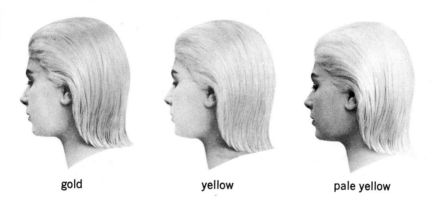

gold   yellow   pale yellow

How Long to Lighten for the New High-Fashion Shades

The first concern of any hairdresser is to leave the patron's hair in the best condition. This is accomplished in two ways:

1. Avoid lightening longer than is absolutely necessary. Lighten at least

45 minutes but, beyond that, no longer than is needed to reach the pre-lightened stage you need for a particular Creme Toner.

2. Use a very fast-acting lightener such as Ultra-Blue Lady Clairol which shortens time and conditions hair as it lightens.

Follow these two rules and you can avoid the hair-weakening and time-consuming lightening. Why reach the yellow stage when the gold stage is as far as you need go for a particular toner shade?

Selection of Lightener for Beautiful Toning Results

There are three Lady Clairol lighteners suitable for use before toning.

1. **Ultra-Blue Lady Clairol Cremogenized Hair Lightener Plus 2 Protinator Envelopes** is the pair especially created for pre-lightening for the Creme Toner. Together they lighten more quickly and lighter than any other product, give the most comfortable lightening treatment in the world, leave hair lighter, drabber—in the best possible condition for high-fashion blonde toning. (See previous chapter for full description.)

2. **Instant Whip Lady Clairol Hair Lightener with 2 Boosters.**

3. **Lady Clairol Whipped Creme Lightener with 2 Boosters.**

Clairol Blue Lightening is an all-purpose lightener in powder form. It is generally not used prior to toning unless hair is extremely resistant. (See page 85.)

How to Lighten Hair for Clairol Creme Toner

Apply lightening mixture as directed on pages 89-90, making color tests until the correct stage of lightening required for the Creme Toner selected is reached.

How Often to Retouch

Your Clairol Creme Toner patrons should not wait too long between retouches. Advise your patrons that if they do, they will have to go through almost as long a pre-lightening period as for the original application. If a patron has her hair retouched before there is too much resistant new growth, she will save herself time and expense.

Dark brown or black hair should be retouched about every ten days. Medium brown hair or hair with a quantity of red pigment should be done every two weeks or so. You may wait three weeks before retouching light brown or blonde hair.

RETOUCH APPLICATION OF PRE-LIGHTENER

See page 91, "Clairol Lighteners" chapter for directions.

POINTS TO REMEMBER IN LIGHTENING FOR RETOUCH

Remember that the lightener should be applied to the new growth only and not carried down the hair shaft. When this is done, breakage may result and the hair may not hold color.

There are three exceptions to this:

1. If a lighter shade is desired, the lightener should be carried through the entire strand when the roots are almost light enough. Leave the lightener on until the shaft has lightened sufficiently.

2. If it is simply another color that is desired, the lightener should be carried through the entire strand after it has developed fully at the roots and just before it is rinsed from the hair.

3. If color has become a little heavy and muddy after two or three retouches, bring lightener through for last 5 minutes. Whenever bringing lightener through, use whatever is left from application. Do not use a fresh mixture.

RESULTS OF IMPROPER PRE-LIGHTENING PRIOR TO TONING

Improper pre-lightening may lead to any of the following results:

1. The hair may have a greenish cast after the application of a Creme Toner with a bluish base.

2. Uneven lightening will result in an uneven finished color. If the hair is unevenly lightened there will be gold bands throughout. These gold bands will show through the Creme Toner shade.

3. Damaged hair will result in breakage.

TIPS TO INSURE CORRECT LIGHTENING FOR PERFECT TONING RESULTS

1. Be sure to rinse the lightening mixture from the hair *thoroughly*. Any left in the hair will actually destroy the color value of the Creme Toner. This happens most often at the front and back hairlines. For this reason it is advisable to give one gentle shampoo at the end of the lightening treatment.

2. Some scalps are extra-sensitive. Never rub the scalp excessively when shampooing the lightening from the hair.

3. Be careful not to leave the hair too wet prior to toning. Too much moisture left in the hair will dilute the color and parts of the hair, particularly the ends, may not receive enough color. Hair should be towel-dried and left just damp before the toning.

HOW TO CORRECT UNEVEN PRE-LIGHTENING

Because of the unevenness of natural pigmentation, hair is often not lightened evenly from the roots to ends. Or this may be due to careless application of the lightening mixture. When this happens, gold bands or spots show through the delicate toner shade.

At the next retouch, after the lightening mixture has been applied to the retouch area, use some of it on the gold-band areas and let it remain until the gold bands or spots have been lightened sufficiently to even out the whole head of hair.

(Or, as a quick (but temporary remedy), see under "Case Histories," Numbers 1 and 2.)

REGULAR RECONDITIONING FOR HIGHLY PRE-LIGHTENED HAIR

Hair that is highly pre-lightened for high fashion blonding should be given regular reconditioning treatments. See Chapter 16 on Reconditioning Hair for information about condition*, Clairol's new conditioner and about Metalex, and how to use them.

HOW TO RECONDITION HAIR WHILE LIGHTENING FOR RETOUCH

Now, with Clairol's new condition*, you can give a conditioning treatment while doing the pre-lightening for a retouch treatment.

1. Apply lightening mixture to the root area.

2. Immediately after application of lightener, apply condition* to the rest of the hair strand. When roots are lightened sufficiently, rinse out. Give a light shampoo if desired.

CHAPTER 9

HIGH-FASHION
BLONDING WITH
CLAIROL CREME TONER

MORE AND MORE fashion-conscious women today are becoming blondes. Blonding is one of the most profitable services the beauty salon has to offer and the 32 delicate blonde shades in Clairol Creme Toner offer this whole range of glamorous choice to every patron no matter what her natural haircoloring. Clairol Creme Toner is the most exciting development in the haircolorist's art.

These blonde colors, such as Silver, Ash, Platinum, Beige, Chiffon, Pearl and Champagne, are perfect for any patron who wants extremely light and delicately colored hair. The lighter silver tones—Silver, Ash and Platinum—have special flattery for women with complexion changes which accompany gray hair and advancing years.

You know from what you've just learned about lightening that it is necessary to pre-lighten hair to the gold, yellow or pale yellow stage in order to apply a Creme Toner successfully. Hair must be lightened to one of these three stages not only to remove the natural pigment but also to make the hair porous enough to absorb the pale blonde Creme Toner color.

Selecting the Creme Toner

The Creme Toner color selected must be one that will do the best coloring job on the degree of lightening and porosity created at the time of the treatment.

Frequently in choosing a high-fashion blonde shade color selection must be left to the haircolorist's judgment, not the patron's, because the result is dependent upon the pigmentation of the hair and how far it can be decolorized. This is especially true in the first or second treatment when some red or gold pigment may remain. When this happens, the Creme Toner must be deeper and not as silvery as the patron would like. The color of her choice might result in a shade with a greenish cast, or the color might not take at all. It may be necessary to give a few additional lightening treatments before the hair is ready for the color the patron wants.

CLAIROL CREME TONER
COLOR SELECTOR
ADDS THE NEW PEARL BLONDES

**Clairol
Creme
Toner**

Creme Toner, an oil shampoo tint, is a permanent, penetrating type of haircoloring and one of the finest tints you can use. It comes in 32 delicate, high-fashion blonde shades. In addition to color, Creme Toner contains a superfine liquid shampoo that cleanses the hair as it colors. It is formulated with fine conditioning oils, leaving the hair soft and lustrous. Creme Toner becomes a creme when the developer is added which gives it the advantage of being easier to work with, since it does not run or dry out.

Toners are tints which are extremely light and delicate. By themselves they do not penetrate and deposit color as quickly and easily as the deeper shades of tints. Therefore, they are completely dependent upon the preliminary lightening which must leave the hair light enough and porous enough.

Pre-Lightening for the Creme Toner Shades

The importance of pre-lightening the hair to the correct one of the final three of the "7 stages of lightening" for the Creme Toner color selected cannot be overemphasized. See chart, page 95.

In the previous chapter, page 96, are outlined the Clairol lighteners suitable for use before toning with a Clairol Creme Toner. Ultra-Blue Lady Clairol Cremogenized Hair Lightener plus Ultra-Blue Protinator is especially recommended. See Chapter 7 on "Clairol Lighteners and What They Do" on pre-testing for lightening, how to mix lighteners and how to apply.

Some shades of Clairol Creme Toner tints require more pre-lightening than others. The table which follows divides the 32 colors into 9 groups according to the base shade and gives you the stage to which the hair should be pre-lightened for each Creme Toner color. By "base shade" we refer to the color the toner is during application and development time. (For instance, Silver Blonde has a bluish cast; Ash Blonde a brownish cast; Platinum a purple cast.)

Clairol Creme Toner Colors and Guide for Lightening

ASH BLONDE COLORS (brown base)—**pre-lighten hair to yellow stage.**

9A Towhead ... Light Ash Blonde
Moonbeam Blonde ... Light-Medium Ash Blonde
10B Sandy Blonde ... Medium Ash Blonde

SILVER BLONDE COLORS (blue base)—**pre-lighten hair to pale yellow stage.**

Extra-Lite Silver Blonde ... Light Silver Blonde
Silver Smoke ... Medium Silver Blonde
Silver Blu ... Deep Bluish Silver Blonde

PLATINUM BLONDE COLORS (purple base)—**pre-lighten to pale yellow stage.**

Extra-Lite Platinum ... Light Platinum Blonde
Silver Platinum ... Medium Platinum Blonde
Smoke Platinum ... Deep Platinum Blonde

NEUTRAL COLORS (gold base)—**pre-lighten to yellow stage.**

Extra-Lite A ... Pale Neutral Blonde
Extra-Lite B ... Light Delicate Golden Blonde

WARM COLOR (reddish-gold base)—**pre-lighten to gold stage.**

Strawberry Blonde ... Light Titian Blonde

BEIGE COLORS ("varied" bases)

GROUP I—pre-lighten to pale yellow stage.
White Beige ... White, White Blonde
Platinum Beige ... Delicate Platinum Blonde
GROUP II—pre-lighten to yellow stage.
Champagne Beige ... Delicate Baby Blonde
Silver Beige ... Silvery Golden Blonde

GROUP III—pre-lighten to gold stage.
Rose-Beige ... Pinkish Golden Blonde
Buttercup Beige ... Rich Golden Blonde

CHIFFON COLORS—pre-lighten to stage a little lighter than the yellow stage but not as light as a pale yellow.

Ivory Chiffon ... Flaxen Blonde
Honey Chiffon ... Honey Blonde
Peach Chiffon ... Peach Blonde
Pink Chiffon ... Pink Blonde

CHAMPAGNE COLORS ("varied" bases)—**pre-lighten to pale yellow stage.**

Champagne Ice ... Almost White
Champagne Sherbet ... Palest Mauvey Blonde
pre-lighten pale yellow to yellow stage
Champagne Parfait ... Softest Lightest Ash Blonde
pre-lighten to yellow stage
Champagne Toast ... Muted Ash Blonde

102

PEARL COLORS ("varied" bases)—**pre-lighten to pale yellow stage.**

Baby Pearl . . . Pale, Pale Beige
Blush Pearl . . . Hint of Mauve
Pastel Pearl . . . Delicate Beige
Sterling Pearl . . . True Silver
pre-lighten to yellow stage
Taupe Pearl . . . Muted Mauve
Tan Pearl . . . Tan Beige

Personalized Shades with Clairol Creme Toner Colors

Intermixing Creme Toner colors offers the true haircoloring artist an opportunity to create custom-made shades. Experiment with color mixing—use the Confidential Mixing Formulas which follow as a guide.

CLAIROL CREME TONER CONFIDENTIAL FORMULAS
MODIFIED SILVER ASH BLONDES

NO.	MIXING FORMULA	RESULTS
1.	1 oz. Extra-Lite A 1 oz. Extra-Lite Platinum 2 oz. Clairoxide or Pure White Creme Developer	A very light silver ash
2.	1 oz. Extra-Lite B 1 oz. Extra-Lite Platinum 2 oz. Clairoxide or Pure White Creme Developer	A light blonde with slight silver tones
3.	½ oz. Silver Platinum ½ oz. Extra-Lite B 2 oz. Clairoxide or Pure White Creme Developer	A light delicate silver ash
4.	1 oz. Silver Platinum 1 oz. Extra-Lite B 2 oz. Clairoxide or Pure White Creme Developer	A delicate silvery ash
5.	½ oz. 11A Light Blonde ½ oz. Silver Platinum 2 oz. Clairoxide or Pure White Creme Developer	A light delicate ash with silver tones
6.	1 oz. 11A Light Blonde 1 oz. Silver Platinum 2 oz. Clairoxide or Pure White Creme Developer	A light ash with silver tones
7.	1½ oz. Extra-Lite A ½ oz. Extra-Lite Platinum 2 oz. Clairoxide or Pure White Creme Developer	A delicate silver ash

103

MODIFIED ASH BLONDES

NO.	MIXING FORMULA	RESULTS
1.	1 oz. 9A Towhead 1 oz. Extra-Lite A 2 oz. Clairoxide or Pure White Creme Developer	A shade slightly lighter and less drab than 9A Towhead
2.	1 oz. Moonbeam Blonde 1 oz. Extra-Lite A 2 oz. Clairoxide or Pure White Creme Developer	A shade a little lighter and less drab than Moonbeam
3.	1 oz. 10B Sandy Blonde 1 oz. Extra-Lite A 2 oz. Clairoxide or Pure White Creme Developer	A shade a little lighter and less drab than 10B Sandy Blonde
4.	1½ oz. 10B Sandy Blonde ½ oz. Extra-Lite A 2 oz. Clairoxide or Pure White Creme Developer	A soft ash blonde

DEEP SILVERY ASH BLONDES

NO.	MIXING FORMULA	RESULTS
1.	1½ oz. 9A Towhead ½ oz. Extra-Lite Silver Blonde 2 oz. Clairoxide or Pure White Creme Developer	A light silvery ash blonde.
2.	1 oz. 9A Towhead 1 oz. Extra-Lite Silver Blonde 2 oz. Clairoxide or Pure White Creme Developer	A silvery ash blonde.
3.	1½ oz. Moonbeam Blonde ½ oz. Extra-Lite Silver Blonde 2 oz. Clairoxide or Pure White Creme Developer	A medium silvery ash.
4.	1 oz. Moonbeam Blonde 1 oz. Extra-Lite Silver Blonde 2 oz. Clairoxide or Pure White Creme Developer	A medium silvery ash.
5.	1 oz. Moonbeam Blonde 1 oz. Silver Smoke 2 oz. Clairoxide or Pure White Creme Developer	A medium smoky ash.
6.	1 oz. 10B Sandy Blonde 1 oz. Silver Blu 2 oz. Clairoxide or Pure White Creme Developer	A deep smoky ash.

LIGHT SILVERY ASH BLONDES

NO.	MIXING FORMULA	RESULTS
1.	1½ oz. 9A Towhead ½ oz. Extra-Lite Platinum 2 oz. Clairoxide or Pure White Creme Developer	A very light ash with delicate silver tones.
2.	1 oz. 9A Towhead 1 oz. Extra-Lite Platinum 2 oz. Clairoxide or Pure White Creme Developer	A delicate silvery ash shade.
3.	1 oz. 9A Towhead 1 oz. Silver Platinum 2 oz. Clairoxide or Pure White Creme Developer	A light silvery ash blonde.
4.	1½ oz. Moonbeam Blonde ½ oz. Extra-Lite Platinum 2 oz. Clairoxide or Pure White Creme Developer	A light ash with slight silver tones.
5.	1 oz. Moonbeam Blonde 1 oz. Extra-Lite Platinum 2 oz. Clairoxide or Pure White Creme Developer	A light silver ash.
6.	1½ oz. Moonbeam Blonde ½ oz. Silver Platinum 2 oz. Clairoxide or Pure White Creme Developer	A light ash blonde with silvery tones.
7.	1 oz. Moonbeam Blonde 1 oz. Silver Platinum 2 oz. Clairoxide or Pure White Creme Developer	A light medium silvery ash shade.
8.	1 oz. 10B Sandy Blonde 1 oz. Silver Platinum 2 oz. Clairoxide or Pure White Creme Developer	A medium silver ash shade.
9.	1½ oz. 10B Sandy Blonde ½ oz. Smoke Platinum 2 oz. Clairoxide or Pure White Creme Developer	A medium ash with smoky tones.
10.	1 oz. 10B Sandy Blonde 1 oz. Smoke Platinum 2 oz. Clairoxide or Pure White Creme Developer	A medium smoky ash blonde.
11.	1 oz. 9A Towhead 1 oz. Platinum Beige 2 oz. Clairoxide or Pure White Creme Developer	A light ash with platinum tones

ASH BLONDES

NO.	MIXING FORMULA	RESULTS
1.	1 oz. 9A Towhead 2 oz. Clairoxide or Pure White Creme Developer	A light ash blonde . . . a little lighter and a little less ash than 9A Towhead.
2.	1 oz. Moonbeam Blonde 2 oz. Clairoxide or Pure White Creme Developer	A light ash blonde . . . a little lighter and a little less ash than Moonbeam Blonde.
3.	1 oz. 10B Sandy Blonde 2 oz. Clairoxide or Pure White Creme Developer	A little lighter and a little less ash than 10B Sandy Blonde.
4.	1 oz. 9A Towhead 1 oz. Moonbeam Blonde 2 oz. Clairoxide or Pure White Creme Developer	A shade a little deeper and drabber than 9A Towhead.
5.	1 oz. Moonbeam Blonde 1 oz. 10B Sandy Blonde 2 oz. Clairoxide or Pure White Creme Developer	A shade a little deeper than Moonbeam Blonde.
6.	2 oz. 10B Sandy Blonde 3 or 4 capfuls 15E 2 oz. Clairoxide or Pure White Creme Developer	A dark ash blonde...deeper and drabber than 10B Sandy Blonde.

PLATINUM BLONDES

NO.	MIXING FORMULA	RESULTS
1.	1 oz. Extra-Lite Platinum 2 oz. Clairoxide or Pure White Creme Developer	A light platinum, a little lighter and less silvery than Extra-Lite Platinum.
2.	1 oz. Silver Platinum 2 oz. Clairoxide or Pure White Creme Developer	A little lighter and a little less silvery than Silver Platinum.
3.	1 oz. Smoke Platinum 2 oz. Clairoxide or Pure White Creme Developer	A little lighter and a little less silvery than Smoke Platinum.
4.	1 oz. Extra-Lite Platinum 1 oz. Silver Platinum 2 oz. Clairoxide or Pure White Creme Developer	A shade a little deeper and a little more silvery than Extra-Lite Platinum.

5.	1 oz. Silver Platinum 1 oz. Smoke Platinum 2 oz. Clairoxide or Pure White Creme Developer	A shade a little deeper and a little more silvery than Silver Platinum.
6.	1 oz. Smoke Platinum 1 oz. Extra-Lite Silver Blonde 2 oz. Clairoxide or Pure White Creme Developer	A shade a little deeper and a little more silvery than Smoke Platinum.
7.	2 oz. Extra-Lite Platinum 3 or 4 capfuls Strawberry Blonde 2 oz. Clairoxide or Pure White Creme Developer	A light platinum with a little less silver than Extra-Lite Platinum.

SILVER BLONDES

NO.	MIXING FORMULA	RESULTS
1.	1 oz. Extra-Lite Silver Blonde 2 oz. Clairoxide or Pure White Creme Developer	A shade lighter and a little less silver than Extra-Lite Silver Blonde.
2.	1 oz. Silver Smoke 2 oz. Clairoxide or Pure White Creme Developer	A shade a little lighter and less silvery than Silver Smoke.
3.	1 oz. Silver Blu 2 oz. Clairoxide or Pure White Creme Developer	A shade a little lighter and a little less silver than Silver Blu.
4.	1 oz. Extra-Lite Silver Blonde 1 oz. Silver Smoke 2 oz. Clairoxide or Pure White Creme Developer	A shade a little deeper and a little more silvery than Extra-Lite Silver.
5.	1 oz. Silver Smoke 1 oz. Silver Blu 2 oz. Clairoxide or Pure White Creme Developer	A shade a little deeper and a little more silvery than Silver Smoke.
6.	1½ oz. Silver Blu ½ oz. Silver Smoke 2 oz. Clairoxide or Pure White Creme Developer	A shade a little lighter than Silver Blu.
7.	1½ oz. Extra-Lite Silver Blonde ½ oz. Strawberry Blonde 2 oz. Clairoxide or Pure White Creme Developer	A light silver with a little less silver than Extra-Lite Silver Blonde.

EXTRA-LITE BLONDES

NO.	MIXING FORMULA	RESULTS
1.	1 oz. Extra-Lite A 2 oz. Clairoxide or Pure White Creme Developer	A very light delicate blonde — lighter than Extra-Lite A.
2.	1 oz. Extra-Lite B 2 oz. Clairoxide or Pure White Creme Developer	A very light delicate golden blonde.
3.	1 oz. Extra-Lite A 1 oz. Extra-Lite B 2 oz. Clairoxide or Pure White Creme Developer	A shade a little deeper and slightly more golden than Extra-Lite A.
4.	1 oz. Extra-Lite B 1 oz. Light Blonde 11A 2 oz. Clairoxide or Pure White Creme Developer	A shade a little deeper and more golden than Extra-Lite B.
5.	1 oz. Extra-Lite B 1 oz. Strawberry Blonde 2 oz. Clairoxide or Pure White Creme Developer	A more golden shade than Extra-Lite B.

BEIGE TONERS

NO.	MIXING FORMULA	RESULTS
1.	1 oz. White Beige 1 oz. Extra-Lite A 2 oz. Clairoxide or Pure White Creme Developer	A very light platinum ash.
2.	1 oz. White Beige 1 oz. Champagne Beige 2 oz. Clairoxide or Pure White Creme Developer	A pale blonde with light golden ash tones.
3.	1 oz. White Beige 1 oz. Platinum Beige 2 oz. Clairoxide or Pure White Creme Developer	A very light platinum blonde.
4.	1 oz. White Beige 1 oz. 9A Towhead 2 oz. Clairoxide or Pure White Creme Developer	A delicate light ash blonde with a slight silver tone.
5.	1 oz. White Beige 1 oz. Extra-Lite Platinum 2 oz. Clairoxide or Pure White Creme Developer	A delicate pearly platinum.

6.   1 oz. White Beige   A blue-white blonde.
         1 oz. Extra-Lite Silver
         2 oz. Clairoxide or Pure White Creme Developer

7.   1 oz. Platinum Beige   A light platinum ash.
         1 oz. Extra-Lite A
         2 oz. Clairoxide or Pure White Creme Developer

8.   1 oz. Platinum Beige   A light platinum ash blonde.
         1 oz. Champagne Beige
         2 oz. Clairoxide or Pure White Creme Developer

9.   1 oz. Platinum Beige   A medium platinum blonde.
         1 oz. Silver Platinum
         2 oz. Clairoxide or Pure White Creme Developer

10. 1 oz. Platinum Beige   A very light ash with delicate
         1 oz. 9A Towhead   platinum tones.
         2 oz. Clairoxide or Pure White Creme Developer

11. 1 oz. Silver Beige   A medium platinum ash
         1 oz. Platinum Beige   blonde.
         2 oz. Clairoxide or Pure White Creme Developer

12. 1 oz. Champagne Beige   A soft baby blonde.
         1 oz. Extra-Lite A
         2 oz. Clairoxide or Pure White Creme Developer

13. 1 oz. Champagne Beige   A medium light platinum ash.
         1 oz. Extra-Lite Platinum
         2 oz. Clairoxide or Pure White Creme Developer

14. 1 oz. Champagne Beige   A deep platinum blonde.
         1 oz. Smoke Platinum
         2 oz. Clairoxide or Pure White Creme Developer

15. 1 oz. Champagne Beige   A light ash blonde with
         1 oz. 9A Towhead   slight gold highlights.
         2 oz. Clairoxide or Pure White Creme Developer

16. 1 oz. Champagne Beige   A medium baby blonde with
         1 oz. Silver Beige   silvery golden highlights.
         2 oz. Clairoxide or Pure White Creme Developer

17. 1 oz. Champagne Beige   A medium blonde with
         1 oz. Rose Beige   slight reddish highlights.
         2 oz. Clairoxide or Pure White Creme Developer

18. 1 oz. Silver Beige   A light silvery golden blonde.
1 oz. Extra-Lite A
2 oz. Clairoxide or Pure White Creme Developer

19. 1 oz. Silver Beige   A medium ash blonde.
1 oz. Silver Platinum
2 oz. Clairoxide or Pure White Creme Developer

20. 1 oz. Silver Beige   A modified pinkish golden
1 oz. Rose Beige   blonde.
2 oz. Clairoxide or Pure White Creme Developer

21. 1 oz. Buttercup Beige   A light delicate golden blonde.
1 oz. Extra-Lite A
2 oz. Clairoxide or Pure White Creme Developer

22. 1 oz. Buttercup Beige   A delicate golden blonde.
1 oz. Extra-Lite B
2 oz. Clairoxide or Pure White Creme Developer

23. 1 oz. Rose Beige   A light blonde with delicate
1 oz. Extra-Lite A   warm highlights.
2 oz. Clairoxide or Pure White Creme Developer

24. 1 oz. Rose Beige   A warm golden blonde.
1 oz. Buttercup Beige
2 oz. Clairoxide or Pure White Creme Developer

25. 1 oz. any of the six Beige shades   A shade with a similar tone,
2 oz. Clairoxide   but several shades lighter
or pure White Cream Developer   than when used with equal
peroxide.

IVORY CHIFFON

NO.	MIXING FORMULA	RESULTS

1. 1 oz. Ivory Chiffon   Light Champagne Beige
1 oz. Champagne Beige
2 oz. Clairoxide or Pure White Creme Developer

2. ½ oz. Ivory Chiffon   Off-White Beige
1½ oz. White Beige
2 oz. Clairoxide or Pure White Creme Developer

3. 1 oz. Ivory Chiffon   Light Platinum Beige
1 oz. Platinum Beige
2 oz. Clairoxide or Pure White Creme Developer

4.	1 oz. Ivory Chiffon	Extra Light Golden Blonde
	1 oz. Buttercup Beige	
	2 oz. Clairoxide or Pure White Creme Developer	

5.	1 oz. Ivory Chiffon	Extra Light Ash Blonde
	1 oz. 9A Towhead	
	2 oz. Clairoxide or Pure White Creme Developer	

6.	1 oz. Ivory Chiffon	Light Moonbeam Blonde
	1 oz. Moonbeam	
	2 oz. Clairoxide or Pure White Creme Developer	

7.	1 oz. Ivory Chiffon	Medium Ash Blonde
	1 oz. 10B Sandy Blonde	
	2 oz. Clairoxide or Pure White Creme Developer	

8.	1 oz. Ivory Chiffon	Delicate Platinum Blonde
	1 oz. Extra-Lite Platinum	
	2 oz. Clairoxide or Pure White Creme Developer	

9.	1 oz. Ivory Chiffon	Delicate Silver Blonde
	1 oz. Extra-Lite Silver Blonde	
	2 oz. Clairoxide or Pure White Creme Developer	

HONEY CHIFFON

NO.	MIXING FORMULA	RESULTS
1.	1 oz. Honey Chiffon	Palest Golden Blonde
	1 oz. Extra-Lite A	
	2 oz. Clairoxide or Pure White Creme Developer	
2.	1 oz. Honey Chiffon	Delicate Golden Blonde
	1 oz. Extra-Lite B	
	2 oz. Clairoxide or Pure White Creme Developer	
3.	1 oz. Honey Chiffon	Light Strawberry Blonde
	1 oz. Strawberry	
	2 oz. Clairoxide or Pure White Creme Developer	
4.	1 oz. Honey Chiffon	Golden Champagne Beige
	1 oz. Champagne Beige	
	2 oz. Clairoxide or Pure White Creme•Developer	
5.	1 oz. Honey Chiffon	Golden Silver Beige
	1 oz. Silver Beige	
	2 oz. Clairoxide or Pure White Creme Developer	

6.	1 oz. Honey Chiffon	Light Golden Rose Beige
	1 oz. Rose Beige	
	2 oz. Clairoxide or Pure White Creme Developer	

7.	1 oz. Honey Chiffon	Light Golden Blonde
	1 oz. Buttercup Beige	
	2 oz. Clairoxide or Pure White Creme Developer	

8.	1 oz. Honey Chiffon	Soft Ash Blonde
	1 oz. 9A Towhead	
	2 oz. Clairoxide or Pure White Creme Developer	

9.	1 oz. Honey Chiffon	A soft Golden Blonde
	1 oz. Champagne Parfait	
	2 oz. Clairoxide or Pure White Creme Developer	

PEACH CHIFFON

NO.	MIXING FORMULA	RESULTS
1.	1 oz. Peach Chiffon 1 oz. Extra-Lite A 2 oz. Clairoxide or Pure White Creme Developer	Extra Light Peach Blonde
2.	1 oz. Peach Chiffon 1 oz. Extra-Lite B 2 oz. Clairoxide or Pure White Creme Developer	Light Peach Gold Blonde
3.	1 oz. Peach Chiffon 1 oz. Champagne Beige 2 oz. Clairoxide or Pure White Creme Developer	Light Titian Gold Blonde
4.	1 oz. Peach Chiffon 1 oz. Silver Beige 2 oz. Clairoxide or Pure White Creme Developer	Medium Titian Gold Blonde
5.	1 oz. Peach Chiffon 1 oz. Rose Beige 2 oz. Clairoxide or Pure White Creme Developer	Deep Titian Blonde
6.	1 oz. Peach Chiffon 1 oz. Buttercup Beige 2 oz. Clairoxide or Pure White Creme Developer	Titian Gold Blonde
7.	1 oz. Peach Chiffon 1 oz. Strawberry Blonde 2 oz. Clairoxide or Pure White Creme Developer	Bright Strawberry Blonde

PINK CHIFFON

NO.	MIXING FORMULA	RESULTS
1.	1 oz. Pink Chiffon 1 oz. Extra-Lite A 2 oz. Clairoxide or Pure White Creme Developer	Extra-Lite Pinkish Blonde
2.	½ oz. Pink Chiffon 1½ oz. Extra-Lite B 2 oz. Clairoxide or Pure White Creme Developer	Light Gold Blonde with Pink Highlights
3.	1 oz. Pink Chiffon 1 oz. Extra-Lite B 2 oz. Clairoxide or Pure White Creme Developer	Light Pinkish Golden Blonde
4.	½ oz. Pink Chiffon 1½ oz. Champagne Beige 2 oz. Clairoxide or Pure White Creme Developer	Champagne Blonde with · Pink Highlights
5.	1 oz. Pink Chiffon 1 oz. Champagne Blonde 2 oz. Clairoxide or Pure White Creme Developer	Pink Champagne Blonde

CHIFFON COLORS INTERMIXED

NO.	MIXING FORMULA	RESULTS
1.	1 oz. Ivory Chiffon 1 oz. Honey Chiffon 2 oz. Clairoxide or Pure White Creme Developer	Very Delicate Golden Blonde
2.	1 oz. Ivory Chiffon 1 oz. Peach Chiffon 2 oz. Clairoxide or Pure White Creme Developer	Light Delicate Titian Blonde
3.	1½ oz. Ivory Chiffon ½ oz. Pink Chiffon 2 oz. Clairoxide or Pure White Creme Developer	Baby Blonde with Pink Highlights
4.	1 oz. Ivory Chiffon 1 oz. Pink Chiffon 2 oz. Clairoxide or Pure White Creme Developer	Pinkish Baby Blonde
5.	1 oz. Honey Chiffon 1 oz. Pink Chiffon 2 oz. Clairoxide or Pure White Creme Developer	Light Blonde with Red-Gold Highlights

6.	1½ oz. Honey Chiffon	Golden Blonde with Pink
	½ oz. Pink Chiffon	Highlights
	2 oz. Clairoxide or Pure White Creme Developer	

7.	1 oz. Honey Chiffon	Pink-Gold Blonde
	1 oz. Peach Chiffon	
	2 oz. Clairoxide or Pure White Creme Developer	

CHAMPAGNE ICE

NO.	MIXING FORMULA	RESULTS
1.	1 oz. Champagne Ice 1 oz. Extra-Lite A 2 oz. Clairoxide or Pure White Creme Developer	Palest, Pale Blonde
2.	1 oz. Champagne Ice 1 oz. Ivory Chiffon 2 oz. Clairoxide or Pure White Creme Developer	Almost Blonde

CHAMPAGNE SHERBET

NO.	MIXING FORMULA	RESULTS
1.	1 oz. Champagne Sherbet 1 oz. Extra-Lite A 2 oz. Clairoxide or Pure White Creme Developer	Pale Blonde
2.	1 oz. Champagne Sherbet 1 oz. Ivory Chiffon 2 oz. Clairoxide or Pure White Creme Developer	Delicate Soft Blonde

CHAMPAGNE PARFAIT

NO.	MIXING FORMULA	RESULTS
1.	1 oz. Champagne Parfait 1 oz. Extra-Lite A 2 oz. Clairoxide or Pure White Creme Developer	Soft Blonde with a touch of Ash
2.	1 oz. Champagne Parfait 1 oz. Ivory Chiffon 2 oz. Clairoxide or Pure White Creme Developer	Light Neutral Blonde

CHAMPAGNE TOAST

NO.	MIXING FORMULA	RESULTS
1.	1 oz. Champagne Toast 1 oz. Extra-Lite A 2 oz. Clairoxide or Pure White Creme Developer	Light Muted Ash
2.	1 oz. Champagne Toast 1 oz. Ivory Chiffon 2 oz. Clairoxide or Pure White Creme Developer	Very Light Muted Ash Very Soft Muted Ash

CHAMPAGNES INTERMIXED

NO.	MIXING FORMULA	RESULTS
1.	1 oz. Champagne Ice 1 oz. Champagne Sherbet 2 oz. Clairoxide or Pure White Creme Developer	Light Sherbet
2.	1 oz. Champagne Ice 1 oz. Champagne Parfait 2 oz. Clairoxide or Pure White Creme Developer	Light Parfait
3.	1 oz. Champagne Sherbet 1 oz. Champagne Parfait 2 oz. Clairoxide or Pure White Creme Developer	Extra-Light Pale Ash
4.	1 oz. Champagne Parfait 1 oz. Champagne Toast 2 oz. Clairoxide or Pure White Creme Developer	Light Soft Muted Ash

WHEN MIXING YOUR OWN FORMULAS BE SURE TO STRAND TEST

As you become expert in haircoloring, you will want to create personalized shades on your own. You may lighten or deepen any of the above Confidential Formulas by changing the proportions slightly. For example, using more of the deeper shade will result in a deeper version. Be sure to Strand Test for color before you apply one of your own mixtures until you are familiar with the results.

Silver Drops in Blonde Toning

Silver Drops, a concentrated drabber, is not to be used by itself but may be combined with the Clairol Creme Toner colors to produce even drabber effects.

CLAIROL SILVER DROPS WITH CREME TONER

NO.	MIXING FORMULA	RESULTS
1.	2 oz. 9A Towhead 2 oz. Clairoxide or Pure White Creme Developer 3 to 6 Silver Drops	Light Silver Ash Blonde
2.	2 oz. Moonbeam Blonde 2 oz. Clairoxide or Pure White Creme Developer 3 to 6 Silver Drops	Medium Ash Blonde
3.	2 oz. 10B Sandy Blonde 2 oz. Clairoxide or Pure White Creme Developer 3 to 6 Silver Drops	Dark Silvery Ash Blonde

How to Apply Clairol Creme Toner

PRELIMINARY

1. Make Patch or Skin Test for hypersensitivity 24 hours before treatment with equal parts Creme Toner to be used in tinting and Clairol Pure White Creme Developer or Clairoxide. (See page 11.)

2. Make Strand Test on lock snipped from patron's hair when you give Patch Test—to determine the final color.

Just before applying Creme Toner:

1. When hair has lightened sufficiently, shampoo gently but thoroughly with Clairol, the colorfast shampoo, Blue for Lightened and Toned Hair, and towel dry.

2. Assemble materials for mixing and application of Clairol Creme Toner shade selected: a full bottle (2 oz.) of Creme Toner and an equal amount of developer (Pure White Creme Developer or Clairoxide), a Clairol Applicator (or mixing bowl, brush or swab, and rattail comb).

MAKE COLOR STRAND TEST

1. Mix a small amount of the Creme Toner color or combination of colors with an equal amount of developer (Pure White Creme Developer or Clairoxide). Be sure to recap bottles immediately.

2. Apply the mixture to a full strand of lightened hair. Allow color to develop for 15 minutes. Rinse, dry with towel and check color. If color is not developed to desired shade, reapply mixture and check again in 5 minutes. Continue checking until desired shade has been reached.

3. Wash and dry. Then examine for desired results. Write down the time it took for color to develop, and use this guide for toning complete head.

How To Mix Creme Toner

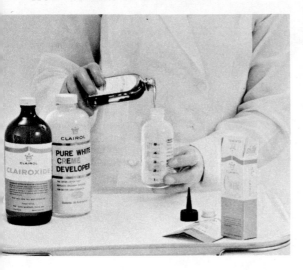

Pour bottle of Clairol Creme Toner into applicator or bowl. Add equal amount of developer (Pure White Creme Developer or Clairoxide). Both should be at room temperature. If you use applicator, cover top with gloved hand and turn it over four or five times. Do not shake. When using bowl, stir mixture gently for just a few seconds.

First Application of Clairol Creme Toner

Be sure hair is pre-lightened to the stage necessary in accordance with the Creme Toner used.

1. Section hair into 4 equal parts using comb or tip of applicator. Outline each section with mixture as you start applying to that section.

2. Starting at the crown with one of the back sections, apply mixture to the root area. Make small 1/8- to 1/4-inch partings.

117

3. When root application is complete, use comb to blend mixture through entire strand, applying additional mixture to saturate hair. (See footnote regarding porous ends.)*

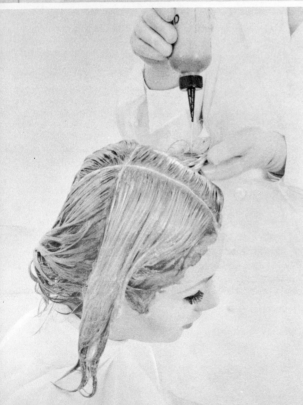

4. Pour any remaining mixture on hair and blend throughout. Do not pack hair down. Leave it loose to permit circulation of air, insuring better color development.

118

5. Fifteen minutes after application is complete, dry a single strand and test for color. If desired color has not been reached, recomb mixture into tested strand. Repeat test frequently until you reach desired shade. Creme Toner will work for 45 minutes.

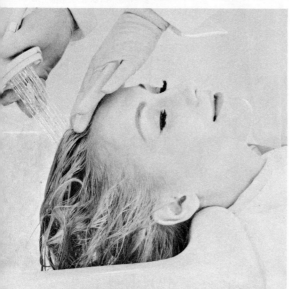

6. When treatment is complete, rinse thoroughly and shampoo with Clairol, the colorfast shampoo, Blue for Lightened and Toned Hair.

*POROUS ENDS. Do not comb Creme Toner mixture through over-porous or damaged ends until the last few minutes of developing time. If Strand Test showed that ends absorb too much color, dilute remaining mixture with equal amount of Clairol Shampoo before applying to ends.

Retouch Application of Clairol Creme Toner
PRELIMINARY

1. Patch Test must be given before application. Also give Strand Test.

2. Pre-lighten new growth only to stage required by Creme Toner.

3. Towel dry hair after lightener has been thoroughly shampooed from hair with Clairol, the colorfast shampoo, Blue for Lightened and Toned Hair. Hair should be slightly damp when Creme Toner is applied.

1. Part hair in 4 sections. Start application at the back of head.

2. Making ⅛- to ¼-inch partings throughout, use a swab, brush or plastic applicator to apply the Creme Toner mixture to the new growth area only.

3. If shaft is holding color from previous treatment, allow the roots to develop to the same degree of color shown by a Strand Test.

Then blend color
through with a comb.
If shaft is almost color-
less, as happens with
lighter, more delicate
shades, then comb color
through immediately.

4. Strand Test fre-
quently. Reapply mixture
to tested strands.

5. When Strand Test
shows almost the
desired shade, work the
balance of the mixture
through the ends.
Should the ends absorb
too much color, dilute
the Creme Toner mixture
with an equal amount of
Clairol, the colorfast
shampoo, Blue for Light-
ened and Toned Hair,
before working through.

6. When color is evenly
developed, as shown by
Strand Test, rinse from
hair and shampoo with
Clairol, the colorfast
shampoo, Blue for Light-
ened and Toned Hair.

121

Tips on Blonde Toning

1. The frequency with which retouches should be given depends, of course, on the rate of hair growth. As a rule, retouches on blonde colors will be more frequent than on ordinary tinted heads because the contrast between the blonde color and the new growth is so great, especially where the hair is naturally very dark.

2. The blonde colors require special care. Because of the intense lightening to which the hair is exposed, it is usually left porous. The color may be easily lifted by improper shampoos and improper treatment. For better color wear, it is advisable to use only Clairol, the colorfast shampoo, Blue for Lightened and Toned Hair.

3. Do not use ordinary creme rinses or heavy pomades and lacquers. Clairol Hair-So-New is ideal to use on blonde hair after the shampoo.

4. During the summer months, the hair should be kept covered to protect it from the sun.

5. Hair toned with the blonde colors should be frequently reconditioned. New **condition*** or Metalex is recommended for this.

Corrective Work

Three things to watch out for in Silver blonding are the following:

1. Complete lack of porosity, resulting in no color take.

2. Hair not lightened to the proper stage. When too many gold tones remain, they may combine with the Creme Toner shade containing blue tones and produce a greenish cast.

3. Hair lightened beyond the stage needed, resulting in more porosity than is necessary. This will cause shades to run too drab, or in severe cases, there is no color take.

HOW TO AVOID OR CORRECT PROBLEMS

All problems encountered by the colorist in blonding can be avoided or corrected when they exist.

1. **Breakage**—This can be avoided by use of Clairol's new **condition*** in conjunction with the lightener. Breakage is caused by overlapping the lightener or leaving the lightener on too long for that particular texture of hair. This can be corrected by a series of reconditioning treatments with **condition*** or Metalex. More attention in the future should be paid to the application of the lightener itself.

2. **Over-silvered hair**—This is due to one of two things. Either the hair becomes too highly lightened and all shades go too dark, or the Silver color selected is too dark. To avoid this, use one of the lightest shades in either the Ash or Silver series or dilute the tint selected with Clairol, the colorfast shampoo, Blue for Lightened and Toned Hair, or additional

developer. To correct a head of hair that has been over-silvered, use any of the following methods:

 a. Apply Clair-Fill, the Clairol filler, choosing one of the warm or red Clair-Fill shades. Color choice depends upon the degree of over-lightening. For example, if color is slightly too drab, use Pale Gold. If color is too dark, choose Brilliant Gold. Apply either before toning or during treatment according to severity of problem.

 b. One application of Metalex without the use of heat. This should remove the necessary amount of Silver. If, however, it fails to do so, a heat cap should be used at moderate temperature.

 c. Shampoo the hair with a mixture of Salon Formula Strawberry Blonde diluted with an equal amount of Clairol, the colorfast shampoo, Blue for Lightened and Toned Hair. (Do not use peroxide.)

 d. Shampoo with mixture of equal parts of Miss Clairol Sun Bronze, Clairoxide or Pure White Creme Developer and shampoo.

 e. Shampoo the hair with a mixture of equal parts of Buttercup Beige, developer and Clairol, the colorfast shampoo, Blue for Lightened and Toned Hair.

3. **Spotting** may exist because of the following:
 a. Drab spots indicate that portions of the hair may have been over-lightened. You can avoid these drab spots by using the new Clairol filler, Clair-Fill, before application of the tint. Another method is to use Creme Toner Strawberry Blonde without the developer. Apply either of the chosen correctives directly to the over-lightened spots. The Creme Toner is then applied directly over it in the usual manner.
 b. Gold spots can be caused by under-lightening. These gold spots can be greatly reduced and final color improved by applying Clair-Fill #7 Platinum filler to these areas.

4. **Dark temples**—If temples become too dark, it is either because the hair is more porous in this section or because the application has been too slow.

 Avoid dark temples by testing the porous areas frequently. As soon as the temples have drabbed sufficiently, gently towel-dry the hair at the temples and hairline. This will retard the action of the tint in these areas.

 Or use Clair-Fill, the new Clairol filler, on these porous areas before application of the tint to avoid darkening result. (Use Clair-Fill shade closest to the color you've been working with.)

5. **Dark ends**—This occurs because ends are over-porous and take color very quickly. Application of one of the Clair-Fill colors to the porous area first, before application of tint, will help avoid this problem. At the same time it will influence the color so there will be even color throughout.

6. Too much blue—In many Silver Blonde treatments on salt-and-pepper hair, it is found that too much blue develops. This is caused by improper selection of color.

When the hair is more than 25% gray, a pure Silver color should not be used. It should be mixed with Ash Blonde to keep the gray hair from turning blue.

The percentage of Silver and Ash in the mixture depends entirely upon the amount of gray in the hair. The amount of Ash Blonde should increase in proportion to the gray in the hair. A Strand Test should be given to determine the exact proportion of Silver and Ash:

> 75% gray—3 parts Ash Blonde (Salon Formula 9A Towhead) to 1 part Silver (Extra Lite Silver Blonde)
>
> 50% gray—Equal parts of Ash Blonde (9A Towhead) and Silver (Extra Lite Silver Blonde)
>
> 25% gray—2 to 3 parts Silver (Extra Lite Silver Blonde) to 1 part of Ash Blonde (Salon Formula 9A Towhead)

7. Drab, off-color results—Use one of the Clair-Fill shades before or after application of toning mixture. Choose the Clair-Fill shade to add color that is lacking.

8. Correction of uneven lightening—If any gold spots remain after the hair is lightened, they must be removed by spot lightening. There may be times, however, when you will not find it practical to spot lighten the hair before applying the toning mixture; the head may be too sensitive for further lightening applications, or there may be too little time left for spot lightening. In these case the gold spots may be overcome as follows:

a. Before toning application, saturate the gold areas with undiluted Clair-Fill #7 Platinum. Wait 5 to 30 minutes. Strand Test until yellow has been sufficiently reduced; rinse and proceed with toning application.

b. During the application of the toner proceed as follows: Mix small quantity of the selected Creme Toner and apply to the gold spots first. Allow to develop 5 to 10 minutes. Then make frequent Strand Tests until you see the gold is almost gone.

Now prepare a fresh mixture of the same toner shade used on the gold spots and apply to the entire head in the conventional manner. Sometimes it may be necessary· to use two different colors to even out the gold spots. Should the gold spots be very heavy, it may be necessary to apply a color one shade deeper than the one selected for the entire head. For example, if the hair has been lightened sufficiently for Silver Platinum, the spots should be tinted first with Smoke Platinum.

It must be remembered that these are only temporary treatments and the gold areas will reappear. At the next treatment the strand should be lightened evenly throughout to eliminate the gold spots.

Do's and Don't's for Creme Toner

Follow the general Do's and Don't's at end of Chapter 2. Before applying a Creme Toner, follow these as well.

Do's

1. Always use Pure White Creme Developer or Clairoxide.

2. Use only glass, porcelain or plastic utensils.

3. Always wear rubber gloves.

4. Mix ingredients at room temperature for best results.

5. Mix Creme Toner immediately before application. (Use a full 2 oz. of Creme Toner and 2 oz. of developer.)

6. Apply Creme Toner as rapidly as possible for even results.

7. Remove excess material from skin gently, without rubbing.

8. Use Clairol, the colorfast shampoo, Blue for Lightened and Toned **Hair,** when diluting Creme Toner or giving final shampoo.

Don't's

1. Don't permanent wave, brush or pre-shampoo hair on day of treatment.

2. Don't apply Creme Toner if scalp has any cuts, sores or abrasions.

3. Don't use Creme Toner on eyelashes or eyebrows.

4. Don't rub skin while removing excess, but gently pat skin with absorbent cotton soaked in bland soap and water solution.

5. Don't reapply within 24 hours.

6. Don't save partially used bottles of Creme Toner. If you mix two Creme Toner shades equally, you may save the remaining 1 ounce of each by combining them (without developer) in a bottle, filled to the top and recapped tightly to keep air out. Label the mixture.

7. Don't store mixture of Creme Toner and developer. It becomes useless and could burst if recapped.

8. Don't use metal dishes.

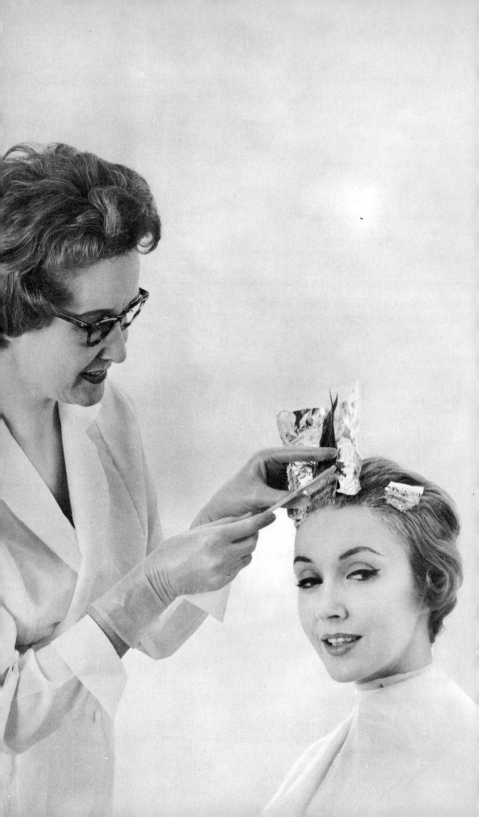

CHAPTER 10

HIGH-FASHION EFFECTS WITH FROSTING, TIPPING, STREAKING AND BLONDE ON BLONDE

S OME OF THE most intriguing and fashionable effects in hairstyling can be achieved by frosting, tipping, streaking and Blonde on Blonde. The first three of these treatments often prepare patrons for a complete blonding treatment since each gives the illusion of light tones. Blonde on Blonde is the latest high-fashion technique to give blonde hair a dramatic pattern of light and dark blonde tones.

Effects You Can Achieve

These four treatments lighten only parts of the hair to contrast with the remainder. The hair may be lightened only a few shades, or it can be made almost white to give the illusion of gray streaks or tips. Sometimes a Creme Toner is used after the lightening.

1. Frosting gives a light effect all over the hair by lightening tiny strands throughout to blend with the darker hair.

2. Tipping gives the same effect as frosting, but lightening is confined to the front of the head. Do not go beyond 2 or 3 inches back from the forehead.

3. Streaking gives dramatic stripes of lighter color around the face by the application of lightener to one, two, three or four attractively placed broad strands of hair.

4. Blonde on Blonde gives somewhat the effect of sun bleaching on blonde hair, but in an artful and sophisticated blending of light and dark blonde tones through haircoloring.

The type of lightening for these effects requires skillful and careful application. It is most important that the lightened parts blend in with the darker hair in a natural, not patterned, manner.

Blue Lightening

Blue Lightening, Clairol's all-purpose powder lightener, is recommended for most of this type of selective lightening. It decolorizes dark hair in the shortest time and works quickly even on resistant hair.

PREPARATIONS FOR FROSTING, TIPPING OR STREAKING WITH BLUE LIGHTENING

The preliminary preparations and mixing of lightener are the same for all these blonding treatments.

1. Do not shampoo hair. Lightening mixture is applied to dry hair.

2. Make Preliminary Strand Test using 1 tsp. Blue Lightening mixed with Clairoxide or Pure White Creme Developer.

3. Study hair style for most attractive lightening effects.

4. Have ready (1) aluminum foil cut into 4- by 5-inch pieces, or (2) Bleaching Cap for frosting or tipping if cap method is preferred.

How to Mix Lightener

Mix in a glass or plastic dish: 2 to 3 tbs. Blue Lightening with enough Clairoxide or Pure White Creme Developer to make a creamy paste of the thickness you prefer. Do not prepare lightening mixture until you are ready to use it.

How to Frost Hair

Using aluminum foil.

1. Pin up all the hair so that it is out of the way, taking care to leave a 1-inch section at the nape of the neck.

2. Beginning at the right side of the hair, proceed to part off a section of hair that measures approximately 1-inch square.

3. Pick up hairs with a fine rattail comb in this 1-inch square section with a darning movement. Weave in and out picking up 6 to 10 strands depending on the degree of frosting desired. There should be about 12 hairs in each of these tiny strands. As you weave in and out, pick up hairs beneath the top layer.

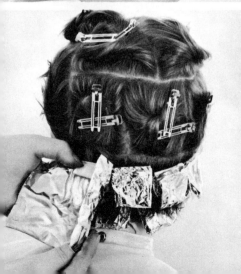

4. Slip hairs off the comb and place a piece of aluminum foil beneath them—as close to scalp as possible.

5. Apply Blue Lightening mixture with brush, starting ½ inch from scalp. Flatten foil and fold up from bottom 2 or 3 times. Continue across the bottom row of hair, preparing 1-inch strands.

6. Start on layer of hair just above the bottom row of hair, patterning rows in checkerboard fashion to avoid regular pattern in completed hair style. Continue working to top and front of head. Omit a layer of hair about ½ inch in width at the front of hairline.

7. Comb hair at the front hairline away from face. Part hair in 1-inch squares. Hold comb parallel to hairline. Continue weaving motion and application of lightener and foil. When head is completely wrapped, place net over entire head and place patron under medium dryer for 10-20 minutes.

8. Test de-colorization on back strand. If hair is sufficiently lightened, remove foil in same pattern as it was applied.

9. Rinse strands individually in soapy water to arrest development.

10. Apply Clairol Creme Toner if desired.

11. Rinse hair and shampoo thoroughly.

How to Tip Hair

Tipping is done just like frosting, only it is confined to the front of the hair. Confine it to the first 2 or 3 inches from the forehead. Begin lightening at the back of area and work toward hairline. Apply lightening mixture and proceed as for frosting.

Cap Method with Blue Lightening for Frosting and Tipping

For a quick method of tipping and frosting, some shops prefer a bleaching cap to aluminum foils. The plastic caps come with perforations already made to simplify the job.

1. With a fine crochet needle pull hair loosely through the holes.

2. Apply Blue Lightening mixture heavily to strands with a brush.

3. Wrap entire head with a large sheet of aluminum foil or cover with a plastic cap.

4. Lightening may be hastened by using a heating cap or placing patron under a dryer. When strands are lightened to desired shade, rinse off while bleaching cap is still on. If toner is to be used, apply now! Then remove cap carefully and shampoo with Clairol, the colorfast shampoo, Blue for Lightened and Toned Hair.

How to Streak Hair

1. Part off strands of hair to be lightened and fasten each with clip or bobby pin. The usual amount of hair for each streak is a strand ½ inch in width and 1 to 2 inches in length.

2. Protect hair behind each strand by applying a heavy cream such as **condition***. For additional protection you may place a piece of cotton behind the strands to be lightened.

3. Place a square of aluminum foil beneath the strand.

4. Apply Blue Lightening mixture to strand, starting ½ inch away from scalp. If ends are damaged do not apply to ends until later.

131

5. Fold foil to cover strand and repeat procedure for remainder of strands.

6. Allow lightener to develop, checking frequently, until strands have reached golden blonde stage.

7. Now apply lightener to hair near scalp and to ends, if they have been excluded. Close foil and allow to develop until the hair is light enough.

8. Unwrap streaks one by one. Dip each in a dish of soapy water as you unwrap to remove lightener and avoid lightening remainder of head.

9. If toning is desired, apply Clairol Creme Toner according to directions to lightened sections.

10. Rinse hair and shampoo at shampoo board.

Suntipping

This is the term given to lightening the hair at the hairline. The same method is used as in streaking, except that smaller sections of hair are lightened and are confined to the hairline area.

1. Part hair lengthwise in section 1/8 inch wide and 2 1/2 in length, beginning at center front of head. Place aluminum foil folded in triangle in back of strand.

2. Apply lightener beginning 1/2 inch away from scalp.

3. Close foil, fold to scalp.

4. Continue procedure until you reach ear, then proceed on other side.

5. Follow streaking instructions for unwrapping, rinsing, toning and shampooing.

Blonde on Blonde
The Latest High-Fashion Style in Haircoloring

The glamorous new Blonde on Blonde effect has wide appeal for fashion-conscious women and offers an opportunity for higher profits to the beauty salon. The soft shadings it gives the hair from pale blonde to dark ash have a dramatic yet very natural look, and it does not need frequent retouching.

Blonde on Blonde has a special and practical appeal for the patron whose hair has been over-lightened or overexposed to sunlight. With this new coloring she can keep the high-style effects while giving her hair a rest.

You probably also have a good prospect for Blonde on Blonde whenever a patron tells you she can't continue her high fashion blonde shade, perhaps because she's Europe-bound or simply has too little time. If you keep the darker color in Blonde on Blonde close to her natural shade, she won't need to retouch for 6 weeks to 2 months or longer.

How To Do Blonde on Blonde
PRELIMINARY

Before you start the Blonde on Blonde treatment, the hair must be a very light, even blonde shade—even dark hair should be lightened to the pale yellow stage. (See Chapter 7.)

To retouch lightened hair, apply Ultra Blue Lady Clairol and 2 Protinators to new growth, usually for about an hour, then to the rest of the hair for 5 minutes. Shampoo with Clairol, the colorfast shampoo, Blue for Lightened and Toned hair, and towel dry.

COLOR FORMULAS FOR BLONDE ON BLONDE

---

1. For the paler color which you use on the whole hair:
Equal parts Clairol Creme Toner Extra-Lite A and Clairol Pure White Creme Developer.

---

2. For the darker color which you use after sectioning off hair and wrapping it in foil:
Combine 1 part Pure White Creme Developer with one part of your choice of the following:

---

a. Equal parts of either Flaxen Blonde or Topaz and Moongold

——————————— or ———————————

b. 2 parts Moongold or 1 part of either Flaxen Blonde or Topaz (this is the most popular)

——————————— or ———————————

c. Moongold

133

Follow These Steps for Blonde on Blonde Color Styling

1. Apply Extra-Lite A to whole head, previously lightened, shampooed and towel-dried. Allow color to develop 10-20 minutes. Rinse, shampoo lightly with Clairol, the colorfast shampoo, Blue for Lightened and Toned Hair.

2. Wrap selected strands, about ¾-inch wide, in aluminum foil. Place foil close to scalp, fold towards center and roll up. Press foil together lightly at base to hold in place. Start with strand at center of hairline, next one at temple, one at ear, and —if you like—one more between temple and ear. Repeat on other side— a total of 7 strands.

3. Continue wrapping strands in foil, working back to nape of neck. Pick up strands in a checkerboard pattern, but make sure there is space between. It takes about 30-45 foils to cover entire head.

4. Apply the second shade (Topaz, Moongold) to all the hair not covered. Be sure to saturate hairline and work color into base of wrapped strands. Allow color to develop 20-30 minutes. Before removing foils, rinse and shampoo carefully. Then remove foils. To retouch Blonde on Blonde: Lighten the whole head and start from the beginning.

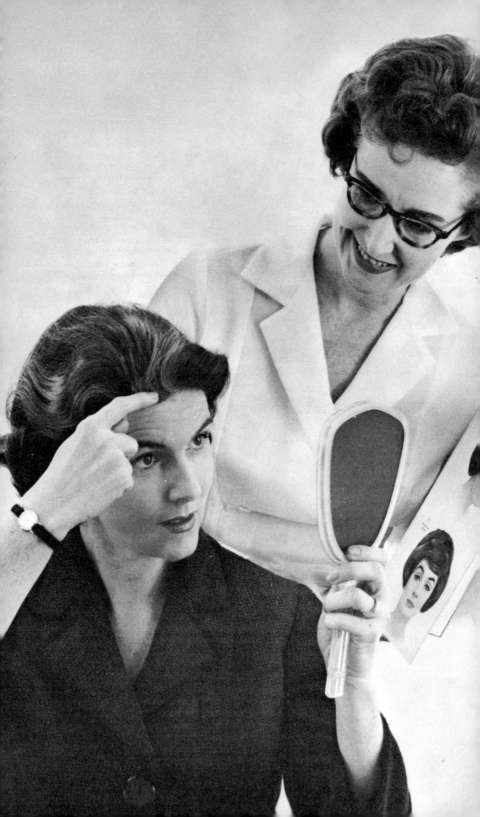

CHAPTER 11

LOVING CARE
HAIR COLOR LOTION

L OVING Care Hair Color Lotion was developed by Clairol Research for the woman with graying hair who will not use tints and can't be satisfied with a rinse. *It washes away only the gray without changing the original natural hair shade.* With the introduction of this hair color lotion, Clairol developed a new category of haircoloring—with unique color results that last through many shampoos. Unlike rinses (which coat hair) Loving Care's natural-looking color gently penetrates and *glows from within* so much like the natural shade no one can tell the difference.

Loving Care contains no peroxide and uses no peroxide. The natural shade remains, only the *gray* is changed. The color is *self-penetrating,* giving the translucent quality that marks natural color. Treatment includes Hair Color Lotion, Plastic Cap, Creme After Rinse.

**Loving Care
Hair Color
Lotion**

Here are some of its advantages that make any operator a colorist:

Contains built-in shampoo. No after-shampoo needed. No pre-shampoo unless hair is extremely soiled or has heavy rinse build-up.

Leaves hair softer, glossier, easy to manage, with a *natural* look.

Color does not rub off. It is self-penetrating to give color that lasts for weeks. Not a tint, yet superior to any rinse.

No retouching needed. Simply repeat the treatment.

LOVING CARE COLORS to match your patron's natural shade

ASH SHADES		GOLD AND WARM SHADES	
73	Ash Blonde	72	Golden Blonde
75	Light Ash Brown	74	Reddish Blonde
77	Medium Ash Brown	80	Auburn
79	Dark Brown	76	Light Golden Brown
83	Natural Black	78	Medium Golden Brown
		82	Dark Warm Brown

Color Selection Tips

1. *For the natural look,* always select the Loving Care color nearest your patron's natural shade.

2. *Colors may be mixed.* You may borrow warm or drab tones according to your need to match natural hair. Partially used bottles of Loving Care may be stored for future use.

3. *When hair is 100% white or gray,* select any color for desired result.

How to Apply Clairol Loving Care
PRELIMINARY

1. Select the color or combination of colors to be used.

2. Make a Patch Test 24 hours before applying.

3. Make a Preliminary Strand Test as follows: Apply the Loving Care shade selected to a full strand of hair. Allow it to develop 30 minutes. Dry with tissue and check color. If desired shade has not been reached in the gray hair, reapply and check again in 15 minutes. Wash and dry hair strand. If shade is still not deep enough, choose the next deeper color in the same shade column.

Application
Shake bottle before using

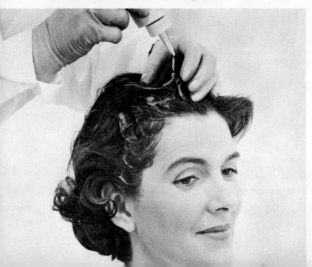

1. Apply to dry hair without shampooing. Use bottle or plastic applicator. Start where there is most gray.

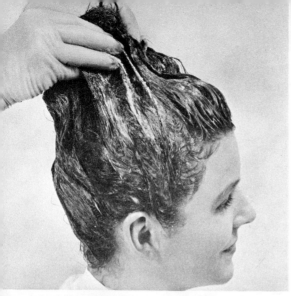

2. Work through the hair with your hands until it lathers, saturating the head thoroughly. Use entire contents of bottle. Do not massage into the scalp. Pile the hair loosely on top of the head.

3. Cover head with plastic cap. Twist edge at forehead and fasten with rubber band or clip. Allow color to develop for 30 minutes.

4. Meanwhile dilute Creme After Rinse in 8 ounces of warm water in cup or applicator.

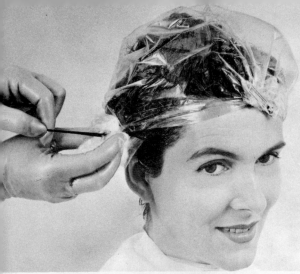

5. After 30 minutes, Strand Test for color development. The first application takes from 30 to 45 minutes.

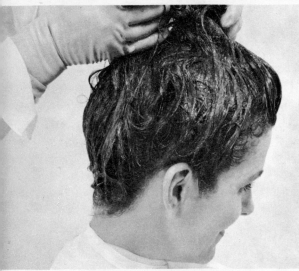

6. When color has developed, wet hair with warm water and work up a lather. Rinse till water runs clear.

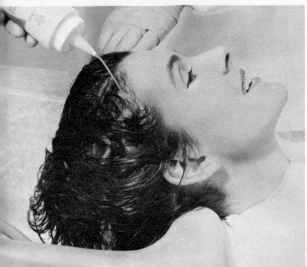

7. Saturate hair with special Loving Care Creme After Rinse. Squeeze out excess, but leave rinse in hair—it's a setting lotion, too.

140

TIMING TIPS

For first application, allow Loving Care to remain on hair from 30 to 45 minutes. On repeat applications usually 30 minutes is sufficient. At 45 minutes the coloring action stops automatically.

How to Keep the Color

Your patron need come in to have the new growth color and general color "refreshed" only about every four or five weeks. Use exactly the same method to apply Loving Care as in the first treatment, except the timing required may be as little as 20 minutes.

If color build-up exists or patron wishes a Loving Care treatment before color has faded away, use this procedure:

1. Apply Loving Care to root area using *large* partings.

2. Put on Plastic Cap and leave on 15 to 20 minutes.

3. Remove cap, apply Loving Care over rest of hair.

4. Put on Plastic Cap and allow color to develop for 10 minutes.

5. Remove cap, wet hair with warm water, work into lather. Rinse.

6. Saturate hair with Creme After Rinse. Squeeze out excess but leave rinse in hair.

HOW TO CHANGE TO A LIGHTER SHADE

To change to a lighter shade, choose a lighter color, allowing 3 weeks (or 3 shampoos) between applications. For an *immediate* change to a lighter shade on the gray, first use Clairol Metalex Special Treatment: Mix 1 part Clairoxide (or Pure White Creme Developer) with 1 part Metalex. Saturate hair with mixture; do not cover. Wait 20 minutes. Rinse thoroughly; shampoo and dry. Apply the lighter color. The Metalex mixture will not lighten the original hair color, merely removes Loving Care shade.

HOW TO CHANGE TO A DARKER COLOR

To change to a darker color after using Loving Care, simply dry the hair, choose the next deeper color and apply immediately as before.

LOVING CARE ON PERMANENT-WAVED HAIR

If hair has not been washed since last permanent wave, shampoo and dry thoroughly before applying Loving Care. Make a Preliminary Strand Test if hair has been permanented since last Loving Care treatment. If test shows deeper color on ends, do not apply Loving Care to this portion of the hair until last 10 minutes of development time. Permanent-waved hair will frequently accept color much faster.

IMPORTANT—Loving Care is specifically for gray or going-gray hair. It is not recommended for lightened or tinted hair. The only exception to this is if previously tinted hair has been tinted with a shade to match the natural shade.

CHAPTER 12

SILK & SILVER
HAIR COLOR LOTION

SILK & Silver Hair Color Lotion bestows new glamour and beauty on the woman with gray or white hair, makes her hair truly a crown of silvery glory. Silk & Silver belongs to Clairol's new category of semi-permanent haircoloring. It is much more than a rinse but not a tint, for it works without peroxide. Yet it is self-penetrating to wash shimmering silver right into each hair shaft and banish "problem yellow," too.

Silk & Silver gives all these wonderful advantages:

Contains Built-in Shampoo, no after shampoo needed, no pre-shampoo unless hair has heavy rinse build-up or is extremely soiled.

Can't Rub Off, can't brush off, can't run off.

Banishes Problem Yellow.

Long-lasting, for a whole month through shampoo after shampoo.

7 Exquisite Silvery Colors, to glamorize every natural shade of gray hair. Won't stain scalp.

Conditions Hair—leaves it silken-soft, manageable, ready to set.

**Silk & Silver
Hair Color
Lotion**

Complete treatment includes Silk & Silver Lotion, Plastic Developing Cap, Creme After Rinse.

SILK & SILVER COLOR GUIDE SELECTOR

FROM LIGHTEST TO DARKEST:	IF HAIR IS WHITE	IF HAIR IS DULL GRAY OR SALT AND PEPPER
Silvery Extra White 10	Lightest sparkling white	Adds lightest white tone
Silvery White 11	Sparkling white tone	Brightens and whitens gray
Silvery Platinum 12	Platinum with mauve shimmer	Adds platinum with mauve shimmer
Silvery Mist 13	Light silver with hint of blue	Gives silvery gleam with hint of blue
Silvery Pearl 14	True gleaming silver	True gleaming silver
Silvery Slate 15	A true slate	A true slate
Silvery Smoke 16	Deep smouldering smoke	Deep smouldering smoke

YOU CAN MIX COLORS—blend any Silk & Silver colors in any proportion to give your patron her choice of silvery color. Silvery Extra White may be mixed with any other shade to create a lighter color effect. When you use a part bottle, the unused portion keeps well.

How to Apply Clairol Silk & Silver Hair Color Lotion

Silk & Silver is always applied to *dry* hair. No pre-shampoo is necessary unless hair is heavily coated with a build-up of temporary rinse or lacquer. Do not use Silk & Silver for lightened or tinted hair.

TIMING CHART

IF HAIR IS	1st APPLICATION	ALL SUBSEQUENT APPLICATIONS
Fine or medium texture	35 minutes	20 minutes
Coarse, wiry, resistant hair	40 minutes	25 minutes
Yellowed or discolored hair	45 minutes	30 minutes or more

PRELIMINARY

1. Select the color or combination of colors to be used.

2. Make a Patch Test 24 hours before applying.

3. Make a Preliminary Strand Test as follows: Apply the Silk & Silver shade selected to a full strand of hair. Allow it to develop 20 minutes. Dry with tissue and check color. If desired shade has not been reached on the gray hair, reapply and check again in 10 minutes. Wash and dry hair strand. If shade is still not deep enough, choose the next deeper color.

Application
Shake bottle before using

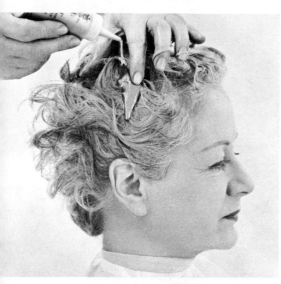

1. Apply to dry hair without shampooing. Use bottle or plastic applicator.

2. Work through the hair with your hands, until it lathers, saturating the head thoroughly. Use entire contents of bottle. Do not massage into the scalp. Pile the hair loosely on top of the head.

145

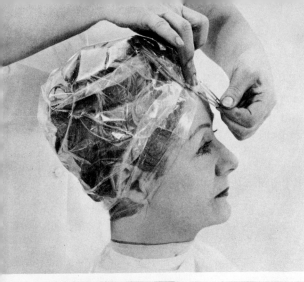

3. Cover head with plastic cap. Twist edge at forehead and fasten with rubber band or clip. Allow color to develop for 30 minutes.

4. Meanwhile dilute Creme After Rinse in 8 ounces of warm water in cup or applicator.

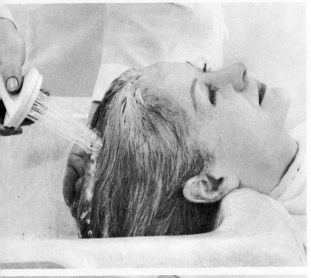

5. Start timing. (See Timing Chart.) Strand Test for color development. The first application takes from 35 to 45 minutes.

6. When color has developed, wet hair with warm water and work up a lather. Rinse till water runs clear.

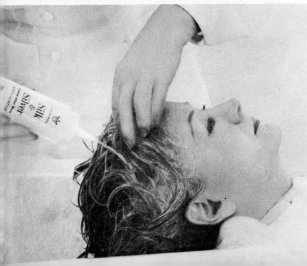

7. Saturate hair with Creme After Rinse. Squeeze out excess, but leave rinse in hair—it's a setting lotion, too.

"REFRESHER" TREATMENT

Your patron need come in only about once a month to have her Silk & Silver color renewed. Follow the same steps as in the first application, with one exception. If you see that the ends are holding too much color from the previous application, omit the ends until the last 5 or 10 minutes of developing time. This is most likely to occur with the deeper shades. Use cap as before.

EXTREME CASES OF PROBLEM YELLOW

Ordinarily 45 minutes development time will correct yellow beautifully. However, in extreme cases, where yellow stain persists the following is recommended:

Apply #12 to the yellowed areas first. This applies *only* when using #10, #11, #13 and #14. (If using #15 or #16 there is sufficient color depth not to require it.) When using #12 a single application is sufficient for this problem.

Put on plastic cap. Wait 10 to 15 minutes. Remove cap, apply Silk & Silver color you are using for the whole head and proceed with treatment.

SPECIAL TIPS FOR PERMANENT-WAVED HAIR

Permanent on ends only. Always make Preliminary Strand Test. If test shows deeper color on ends, do not apply Silk & Silver to this portion of hair until last 10 minutes of development time. No cap is necessary for these last 10 minutes.

On new permanent. If hair has not been shampooed since last permanent or if you have just given a permanent, shampoo and dry hair thoroughly before using Silk & Silver. Make a Preliminary Strand Test to determine timing. Permanent-waved hair will frequently accept color faster so you may want to cut down on timing.

On a Silk & Silver user with a new permanent wave add a small amount of #10 to the shade she is wearing to lighten it a little and thus avoid too much color-take due to porosity. Strand Test first to determine the amount of #10 to use in the mixture.

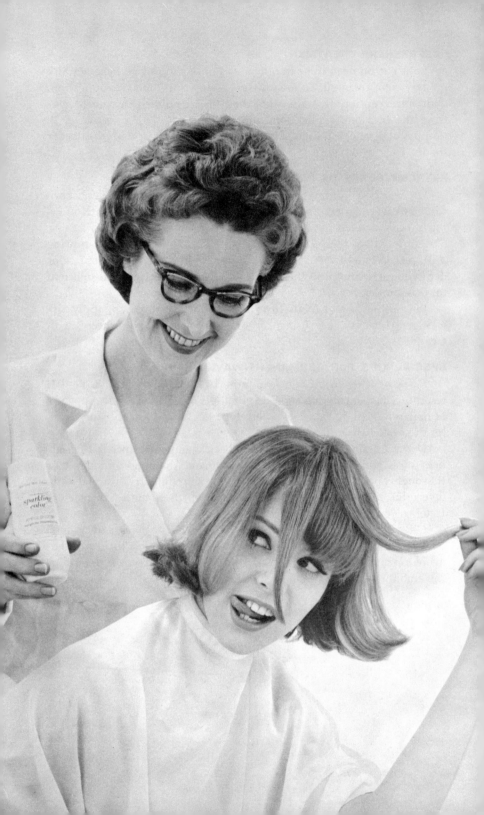

CHAPTER 13

SPARKLING COLOR
HAIR COLOR LOTION

SPARKLING Color Hair Color Lotion, a new semi-permanent haircoloring, is specifically formulated for women *without gray* hair. It glamorously *brightens* and *highlights* natural haircoloring or adds a touch of new color. When hair has gone dull and mousey, or looks "washed out" or faded, a Sparkling Color treatment will reclaim its color beauty.

SPARKLING COLOR is for your patrons without gray

• Who have never had haircoloring applied

• Who have temporary haircoloring applied

• Who have semi-permanent coloring applied
      Do *not* use Sparkling Color on hair that has been lightened or tinted or is mixed with gray. It is chemically formulated for hair *without gray* only.

Sparkling Color Hair Color Lotion

The only one of its kind, Sparkling Color is a Clairol discovery to glamorize hair untouched by gray. One ounce is all that's required for a treatment on average length or short hair. No other extras are needed. Since Sparkling Color does not lighten the hair, the degree of change possible depends on the patron's own natural hair color. On naturally *light* hair, color results will be brighter. On naturally *dark* hair, color results will be softer and more subtle.

IF NATURAL HAIR COLOR IS . . .

SPARKLING COLOR	BLONDE BUT "DULL"	RED BUT "FADED"	LIGHT OR MEDIUM BROWN BUT "MOUSEY"	DARK BROWN OR BLACK BUT "FADED"
SPARKLING BLONDE	intensifies natural color, adds shimmering golden highlights		gives subtle golden glints and lustre	
SPARKLING COPPER	adds vivid light copper highlights	enhances color, with lovely red highlights	brightens natural color with light red glints	adds a touch of soft red highlights and sparkling lustre
SPARKLING MEDIUM AUBURN	imparts a true, rich red color, with dazzling lights and lustre	brightens natural color with exciting auburn highlights	adds glowing depth and dancing auburn highlights	brightens hair, adds subtle warm red glints
SPARKLING DEEP AUBURN	adds deep glowing auburn tones and sparkling highlights	deepens color to full, rich auburn	gives rich, deep auburn tone and glowing lustre	adds gleaming auburn sparkle and lustre
SPARKLING LIGHT BROWN	gives softly shining brown tones and highlights		enlivens natural color with gleaming soft brown highlights	adds brown lustre and sparkle to dull hair
SPARKLING MEDIUM BROWN	adds lustrous brown highlights		intensifies and brightens to full, rich brown	makes hair rich with gleaming brown lustre
SPARKLING DARK BROWN	gives a rich, true brown		deepens color to a glowing brown	brightens color, imparts a true dark, warm brown tone

SPARKLING COLOR OFFERS THESE ADVANTAGES:

7 sparkling colors for blondes, brunettes and redheads to make natural hair shades more brightly beautiful, by adding long-lasting color highlights.

Long-lasting through a whole month of shampoos. Color wears away evenly and gradually with no line of demarcation.

Conditions, improving body and texture, adding bounce and imparting a wonderful lasting softness and lustre.

Contains no peroxide, and no peroxide or other developer is needed.

Won't rub off—it's self-penetrating. Doesn't coat the hair, doesn't stain scalp.

Easy to use. No plastic cap or after-rinse is required in application.

How to Apply Sparkling Color

PRELIMINARY

1. Select the color to be used.

2. Make a Patch Test 24 hours before applying.

3. Preview color if desired with a Preliminary Strand Test.

NOTE: *Do not use* Sparkling Color for lightened or tinted hair or for hair that is mixed with gray.

Application

Shake bottle before using

1. Pre-Shampoo hair, and blot off excess water with a towel. Put on rubber gloves. Shake bottle well.

2. Apply Sparkling Color directly to the hair with applicator. Use 1 ounce of Sparkling Color. Distribute it as evenly as possible.

151

3. With fingers gently work color through the hair until it is thoroughly saturated and a rich lather is formed. Do not rub into scalp.

4. Comb hair through with a wide-toothed comb to assure even distribution. Pile hair lightly on top of head and start timing.

5. The timing. Allow 10 minutes for slight color highlights. Allow 15 minutes for medium color highlights. Allow 20 minutes for more intense color highlights.

6. Strand Test for color. If hair is in poor condition, start Strand Testing after 5 minutes and at 5-minute intervals thereafter. Strand Test by drying a thin strand of hair with a tissue and examining it for evenness and depth of color. If greater color is desired, reapply Sparkling Color to test strand and continue timing.

152

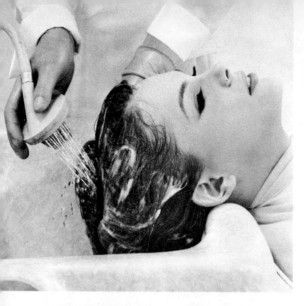

7. When desired color is reached, add a little water to hair and work into a lather, re-wetting any areas along hairline where material may have dried.

8. Rinse hair thoroughly with lukewarm water. Continue rinsing until water runs clear. No additional shampoo is necessary. No cap or after-rinse of any kind is required. Hair is now ready for setting.

Special Tips

Want deeper color? Should greater color effect be desired, a second application of Sparkling Color in the same or a deeper shade may be made immediately.

Want to remove Sparkling Color? If you wish to remove the Sparkling Color shade you have applied, some excess color may be lifted from the hair with Clairol Metalex.

No retouching procedure. Sparkling Color is applied the same way every four weeks.

SPARKLING COLOR ON PERMANENT WAVED HAIR

You may apply Sparkling Color with excellent results before or after permanent waving.

On new permanents. Since newly permanent waved hair absorbs color rapidly, special attention should be paid to timing. Be sure to Strand Test immediately after application is completed, and continue Strand Testing at frequent intervals. As soon as desired color is achieved add water and work material into a quick lather. Then rinse hair thoroughly with lukewarm water.

On older permanents. Strand Test a few minutes after application is completed. If you notice permanented ends have a tendency to absorb color faster than body of hair, remove material from these ends with a damp towel or tissue and continue normal timing.

CHAPTER 14

COME ALIVE
RINSES

WITH Clairol Come Alive Rinses you have a superior temporary hair beautifying service to delight your patrons with glamorous color, silkiness and sparkling highlights. Color stays true till the next shampoo.

There are two Come Alive color groups:

1. Come Alive Gray Rinses give every type of gray hair—from white to pepper-and-salt—shining new silvery beauty ... banish yellow discoloration.

2. Come Alive Colors give color coverage to turning-gray hair, brighten natural or tinted hair and give it brilliant highlights.

Come Alive Gray

These miracle-working rinses are simple and quick to use and make gray hair a thing of radiant beauty. Yellow is banished, and the hair takes on the silvery tone most becoming to your patron, with no blue or purple cast.

4 GLAMOROUS GRAY SHADES

These shades give highlight and sheen for all gradations of gray. For greater variation in personalized color any of these shades, except Midnight Opal, can be mixed together.

1. White Sapphire—This is the *lightest* shade. It adds a brilliant pearly glow to white and almost-white hair.

155

2. Silver Diamond—This is a *medium* shade. It polishes white and gray hair to gleaming silver.

3. Black Pearl—This is a *medium deep* shade. It adds sparkle as it evens tones of salt-and-pepper gray.

4. Midnight Opal—This is the *deepest shade.* It adds lustre as it conceals gray with rich, smoky tones.

MIXING CHART FOR COME ALIVE GRAY

With each shade of Come Alive Gray you can obtain various degrees of color ranging from light to medium to dark.

COLOR DESIRED	ON WHITE HAIR	ON SALT-AND-PEPPER HAIR
For LIGHT COLOR all shades	½ oz. color plus 3 oz. hot water	½ oz. color plus 2½ oz. hot water
For MEDIUM COLOR all shades	½ oz. color plus 2½ oz. hot water	½ oz. color plus 2 oz. hot water
For DEEP COLOR all shades	½ oz. color plus 2 oz. hot water	1 oz. color plus 3 oz. hot water

To make color *deeper,* add *more* Come Alive Gray. To make color *lighter,* add *more* hot water.

Color Mixing

With the exception of Midnight Opal, Come Alive Gray colors can be mixed together for greater variation. For instance, mix White Sapphire with Silver Diamond for a shade halfway between Platinum and Silver.

How to Mix:

1. Always shake bottle before use. *This is particularly important when using Midnight Opal,* since it is more concentrated and can be diluted to a greater degree than the other three Come Alive Gray shades.

2. Mix color with HOT water, the hotter the better, in proportions given on the bottle. Accurate measuring in glass or plastic measuring cup or Miss Clairol Applicator is important. Make 3 to 4 oz. of mixture to assure saturation of entire head of hair. Allow to cool to comfortable temperature. For very yellow discoloration, make mixture more concentrated and apply to that area. Then dilute for the rest of the hair.

How to Apply Come Alive Rinses

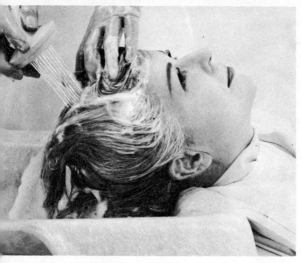

Preview color if desired with Preliminary Strand Test.

1. Shampoo and rinse hair. Towel dry. Shake bottle of Come Alive Gray thoroughly, especially Midnight Opal. Also Blonde, Brown and Red.

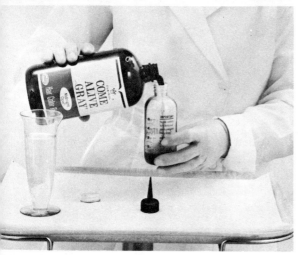

2. Make your mixture diluting with the necessary amount of hot water for the desired result.

3. Apply to hair with brush, cotton swab or plastic applicator. Start on portion of the hair nearest the scalp. Make sure all strands are saturated. If ends are porous, dilute mixture just before applying to ends.

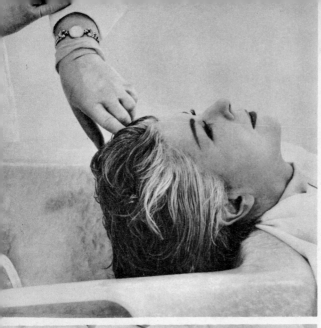

4. Time the development. Allow Come Alive Rinse to remain on the hair from 2 to 5 minutes to get the full effect of the iridescent colors. For a deep shade, use the full 5 minutes.

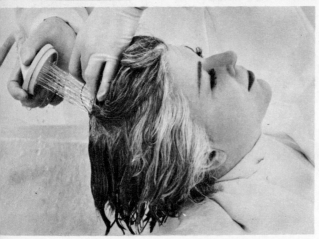

5. Rinse thoroughly with warm water until the water runs clear. This thorough rinsing is important to help keep Come Alive Rinse from rubbing off.

Come Alive Red, Brown and Blonde

All three Come Alive Colors offer important improvements in the field of temporary rinses because they give *more* color without the coated or heavy look some products produce. Use them with more perfect results for the following effects:

Brilliant highlights for natural or tinted hair the same shade.

Color coverage for blending in of gray hair.

Like Come Alive Gray Rinses, these colors stay color-true from shampoo to shampoo, leave hair beautifully conditioned, easy to comb and set, easy for the patron to handle between shop visits.

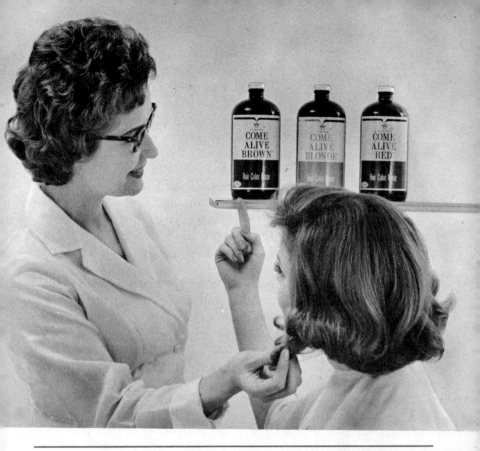

SHADE SELECTOR AND MIXING CHART
FOR COME ALIVE COLORS

SHADE NAME	FOR A LIGHT SHADE	FOR A MEDIUM SHADE	FOR A DARK SHADE
COME ALIVE BLONDE	½ oz. color 8 oz. hot water	½ oz. color 3 oz. hot water	1 oz. color 4 oz. hot water
COME ALIVE RED	½ oz. color 8 oz. hot water	½ oz. color 3 oz. hot water	1 oz. color 4 oz. hot water
COME ALIVE BROWN	½ oz. color 8 oz. hot water	½ oz. color 3 oz. hot water	1 oz. color 4 oz. hot water

General Rule: To make color **deeper,** add **more** Come Alive Rinse. To make color **lighter,** add **more** hot water. The above 3 shades must be shaken well in the bottle before use.

Colors may be intermixed for specialized color effects. (For instance, equal parts of Come Alive Blonde and Come Alive Red produce a reddish gold shade.)

Mixing and Application—follow directions for Come Alive Gray.

159

Other Uses for Come Alive Gray

1. **As an "in-between" toning treatment** on Silver or Ash Blonde hair. Can be used to freshen faded hair. Use *White Sapphire* for light Platinum, White or Platinum Beige shades. Use *Silver Diamond* for light Silver, Silvery Ash or Light Ash Blonde shades. Use *Black Pearl* for dark Ash Blonde or deep Smoky Silver shades.

2. **To tone hair after lightening.** Come Alive Gray is useful when patron must be sent home before the decolorization process is complete to make hair more presentable temporarily. Use *White Sapphire* if you wish to keep hair as light as possible. Use *Silver Diamond* if you want some depth of color or there is a great deal of gold or brassiness.

3. **Use as a toner** on women who may be sensitive to regular tints. With sensitive patrons always give the Patch Test before using Come Alive Gray.

4. **Use to drab red or gold tones** caused by sun-bleaching or permanent waving. Come Alive Gray can also be used to modify red or gold tones on tinted hair between or after treatments.

5. **As a spot toner** to reduce gold spots temporarily. Sometimes there are sections of the hair which are insufficiently drab after a lightening or toner treatment. You may apply Come Alive Gray to these affected areas to even the shade somewhat. Use *White Sapphire* on extremely light shades of hair and *Silver Diamond* on the deeper Silver or Ash colors. If areas are extremely brassy, do not rinse hair after application of Come Alive Gray. Otherwise, give an after-rinse of clear water. This is a *temporary* correction. In order to even the color on the strand, you will have to apply a lightener to the affected areas.

Note: Come Alive Rinses are harmless to the normal scalp and skin. Nevertheless, like the purest food, it may produce an allergic reaction in a susceptible person. If there is any sign of an allergic scalp irritation after using this product, discontinue its use until proper patch testing shows that this product is not the cause of that irritation.

Come Alive Rinses must not be used for dyeing the eyebrows or eyelashes because of the possibility of an allergic reaction of the delicate orbital tissues.

CHAPTER 15

COMBINING TINTING WITH PERMANENT WAVING

S INCE ALMOST every salon patron, except those with naturally curly hair, has a permanent wave, the chances are that most of your tint patrons will be permanent-wave customers as well.

Both permanent waving and haircoloring involve changes in the chemistry of the hair, so it is important to know how these react on each other, and how to schedule permanent waving and coloring treatments.

Always Give the Permanent First, Then Apply the Tint

Give the permanent *first* because permanent waving always changes the color of tinted hair somewhat. This rule applies both to hair that has never been tinted or lightened and to tinted or lightened hair in need of a retouch.

For best results wait a week after the permanent wave before applying hair color. If not possible, allow at least a day or two to elapse between permanent and tint application.

When giving a first color treatment after a new permanent, it is advisable that hair is shampooed once. This will remove any chemical left in the hair.

PROCEDURE WHEN PERMANENT AND TINT MUST BE GIVEN THE SAME DAY

Although it is not advisable to give both treatments the same day, it is sometimes necessary. Greater care than usual should be taken.

1. Give the permanent wave first.

2. Be sure to make a Preliminary Strand Test to determine development time and shampoo dilution necessary for final soap cap.

3. Frequent strand testing during the color treatment is essential because color will develop more rapidly after a permanent wave.

4. Dilute tint with a greater amount of shampoo when giving final soap cap. (Preliminary Strand Test will determine degree of dilution.)

5. If pre-lightening is required, lighten first, then give permanent and finally apply tint.

PROCEDURE WHEN HAIR HAS BEEN TINTED
AND PATRON WISHES A PERMANENT

It is advisable to wait at least 24 hours before giving the permanent. During this 24-hour period, the color has a chance to set. This reduces the possibility of the waving lotion solution or neutralizer causing too great a change in color.

PERMANENT-WAVE LOTIONS FOR TINTED AND LIGHTENED HAIR

Because the problem exists of giving permanent waves on hair that has been previously tinted or lightened, manufacturers of permanent-wave lotions have developed special permanent-wave lotions (weaker than those for normal hair) to be used on tinted or lightened hair. Tinted or lightened hair is usually more porous than normal hair and has a tendency to curl more quickly. The special, weaker lotion compensates for this quicker curling. Even weaker are the special permanent-wave lotions offered for highly lightened hair.

In taking a test curl on tinted or lightened hair, you may find even the weakest lotion causes hair to curl too quickly and too much. In this case the lotion should be diluted even further with water.

PERMANENT WAVING ON HIGHLY LIGHTENED HAIR

First, you must determine to what extent this hair has been over-lightened before a permanent is given. There are two ways of doing this:

1. When wet, over-lightened hair is recognized by its gummy texture and by the fact that it mats easily.

2. If test curl shows hair breakage, over-lightening is indicated.

In either case no permanent wave should be given until after hair has been reconditioned. (Chapter 16 gives two methods of reconditioning hair.)

It is possible that a permanent wave can be given in some cases of over-lightened hair. This is determined by the *test curl*.

IMPORTANCE OF TEST CURL

Many of the problems in permanent waving tinted and lightened hair may be avoided through proper use of the test curl. It helps pre-determine the final results of the permanent wave and also helps you determine what preliminary steps, such as reconditioning, are necessary before the application of the permanent-wave lotion.

CHAPTER 16

RECONDITIONING
HAIR

THE "BIG THREE" services in any beauty salon today are tinting, lightening and permanent waving. Beautiful results with any of these services depend on hair that has been properly conditioned to receive them. You have to consider not only the natural condition of the patron's hair but various "foreign" substances which may have caused damage or be present in the hair.

Women today are experimenting more than ever before with lacquers, metallic powders, color crayons, color sprays, color shampoos and other products which coat the hair. Almost all patrons who come into your salon have used one or more of these products. These products may either be present and not be removed by shampooing alone, or they may have caused damage to the hair which results in lack of penetration of a tint or lightener or breakage and discoloration during a permanent wave. In either case the problem calls for reconditioning.

OTHER "PROBLEM" CONDITIONS

Hair may be damaged by causes other than coating products—overexposure to sun and salt water . . . over-lightening that makes it brittle . . . poor systemic condition or neglect that makes the hair dull and lifeless, dry, thin and unmanageable. These, too, call for correction. Clairol Research has developed a family of products specifically designed for reconditioning various kinds and degrees of damage to hair the use and application of which will be described. But first . . .

How Can You Recognize Damaged Hair?

You can always find out whether hair is damaged or not by first giving a Preliminary Strand Test for color or a test curl before permanent waving. Hair is considered damaged and in need of reconditioning when:

1. The structure, texture and elasticity of the hair have been affected to the extent that it is brittle, broken, matted or split.

2. It is gummy and has lost its elasticity.

3. It is over-porous.

Specialized Clairol Products for Reconditioning Hair

Whatever the cause or the condition of hair damage, Clairol Research offers a product designed to correct it. With these reconditioning aids you can take pride in the soft, shining beauty of your patrons' lightened, tinted or permanent-waved hair. These products are:

condition*

The Beauty Prescription for Troubled Hair

This is Clairol's newest contribution to hair beauty. It is a rich cream compounded to revitalize "tired" hair—dried out, limp or spongy, perhaps with broken ends or damaged areas. Use it as a general reconditioner or in conjunction with lightening and tinting treatments.

Metalex

Metalex is an oil-base solution that restores spring and sheen to hair abused by over-lightening, over-permanenting or home use of certain hair preparations. Metalex *lifts* metallic-based dyes and rinses, compound hennas and hair restorers that coat the hair and often cause discoloration when a permanent or tint is used. Use Metalex as a regular conditioning treatment to give healthy texture and gloss to the hair. Use it to recondition the hair and remove coatings to prepare for successful application of lightener, tint or permanent.

When and How to Use the Clairol Conditioners

I. condition*

Use **condition*** these 3 ways.

A. condition*
As General Treatment To Revitalize Texture, Add Body—A Pre-Permanent "Must"

1. Shampoo and towel dry hair.

2. Apply **condition*** liberally to hair and scalp (about 1½ oz. for average head of hair). Leave cream on hair 20 to 30 minutes. **condition*** does its job without heat.

3. Rinse well.

B. Use condition* While Lightening Hair

1. Apply lightener to roots.

2. Immediately apply **condition*** to the rest of hair strand.

3. When roots are lightened sufficiently, rinse out.

4. Give a light shampoo if desired.

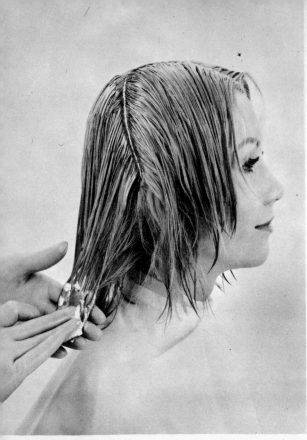

C. Use condition* While You Tint or Tone

1. On towel-dried hair, apply **condition*** sparingly to abused areas (not to the roots). About 1 tbs. is sufficient.

2. Then apply tint or Creme Toner to roots.

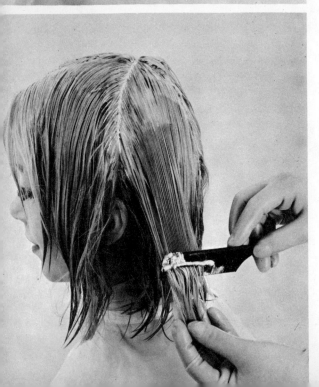

3. When color develops sufficiently in root area, blend color down over **condition***. Develop until color is even.

4. Rinse and shampoo.

166

II. Metalex

Use Metalex for effective reconditioning treatments and also to *remove* all the coating and foreign matter from the hair. Metalex will not remove penetrating color; you may use it to precondition damaged tinted hair for lightening, coloring or a permanent wave. Here are some specific uses you will find valuable:

A. To lift metallic-based dyes and rinses, compound hennas, lacquers, etc., which coat the hair. Reconditions at the same time.

B. To correct a coloring treatment where hair has gone a little darker than desired, if applied immediately after treatment.

C. To improve and restore the quality of the hair between lightening applications.

D. Metalex treatments given to new permanents soften the hair without loosening the curl.

1. Always use Metalex full strength just as it comes from the bottle. Do not dilute it or mix it with any other substance.

2. Apply to hair with generous-sized cotton pads or small paint brush. Apply generously to hair (do not apply on scalp). Be sure to saturate the entire length of hair strand from root to end in the rich oils. Two ounces should be sufficient for one Metalex treatment.

167

3. Work through hair thoroughly. Do not massage into scalp. Pile hair on top of head and wrap in waxed paper.

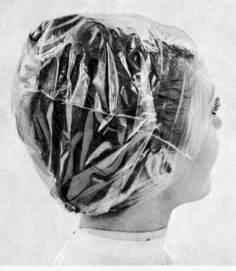

4. Fit a heating cap or a warm towel over waxed paper. For best results heat should be applied for 30 minutes. If warm towel is used, have extra towels heating to replace as towel cools. After half an hour, rinse hair thoroughly with warm water. Metalex rinses out quickly and easily. Shampoo with Clairol Shampoo. Dry and set.

On high fashion blonde hair the heat cap is not necessary.

168

CHAPTER 17

HAIR CARE
WITH CLAIROL
SPECIALIZED PRODUCTS

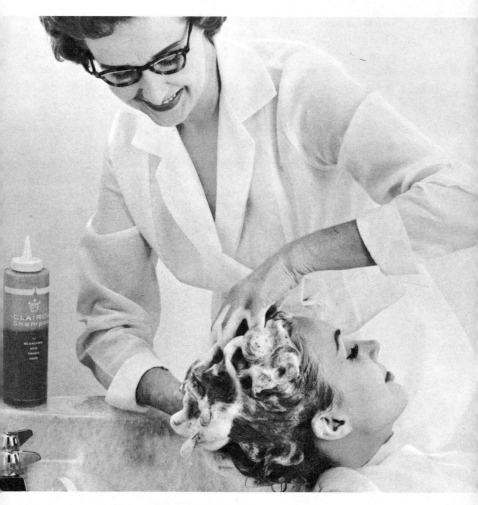

Clairol, the Colorfast Shampoo—
Hair-So-New—Vitapointe

THERE ARE important differences you should understand between hair that has been tinted, and lightened and toned hair. Each type needs special care to stay in good condition and keep color alive and fresh.

To meet this need Clairol Research has formulated products to give the finishing touches that mean satisfied patrons.

Clairol, the Colorfast Shampoo, in 2 Formulations

New Clairol Shampoos are a revolutionary new concept that takes into account the *different* structure and needs of these two hair types. Each does what no ordinary shampoo can do.

Structure of Tinted Hair

Tinted hair is more heavily pigmented than lightened and toned hair. Yet it has undergone enough pre-softening so that ordinary shampoos will strip color. Tinted hair retains more of its strength and elasticity, more natural oils, and so needs less conditioners in a shampoo, but it requires more gentle handling than naturally pigmented, untreated hair.

Clairol Green Shampoo

Clairol Shampoo The Colorfast Formula, Green for Tint and Lasting Rinse Users

This shampoo is especially formulated to guard delicate haircoloring; it protects the color in hair treated with Miss Clairol or other hair-colorings, color shampoos or Hair Color Lotions. It has greater cleansing action because tinted hair is stronger and more heavily pigmented than lightened and toned hair. Because tinted hair is less porous, less conditioning action is needed.

Structure of Lightened or Lightened and Toned Hair

Lightened and toned hair is extremely delicate. Most of the natural pigment has been removed. The hair is left porous and easily penetrated by shampoos and lotions that strip color. It is often spongy and easy to break when wet . . . hard to comb and set. It requires extremely gentle cleansing and the nourishment of rich conditioning ingredients to look and behave best.

Clairol Blue Shampoo

Clairol Shampoo—Colorfast Formula, Blue for Lightened and Toned Hair

This shampoo is specially formulated so it will not strip color from even the most delicate shades. So gentle it provides *extra* conditioning action vital to this more fragile, more porous type of hair.

CLAIROL SHAMPOOS HAVE THESE OTHER VIRTUES OF A SUPERIOR SHAMPOO AS WELL

1. Cleanse better.

2. Condition better.

3. Make richer lather in hard or soft water.

4. Rinse easily.

5. Leave hair silky-soft, easy to manage.

6. Add lustrous highlights to enhance hair color.

7. Economical—each 16 oz. bottle of concentrate makes a full gallon of shampoo.

ADDITIONAL USES FOR CLAIROL SHAMPOOS

Clairol Shampoos need not be limited to tinted hair and lightened and toned hair. You will find them a great help in improving many hair and scalp conditions such as those listed below. For mild cases, use Clairol, the colorfast shampoo, Green. For more advanced cases, use milder Clairol, the colorfast shampoo, Blue.

1. Hard-to-rinse hair with dry, scaly scalp.

2. Dry, porous, over-permanented hair.

3. Damaged hair, left lifeless and brittle.

4. Very fine hair, hard to handle when wet.

5. Hair dry and porous from over-exposure to sun and salt water.

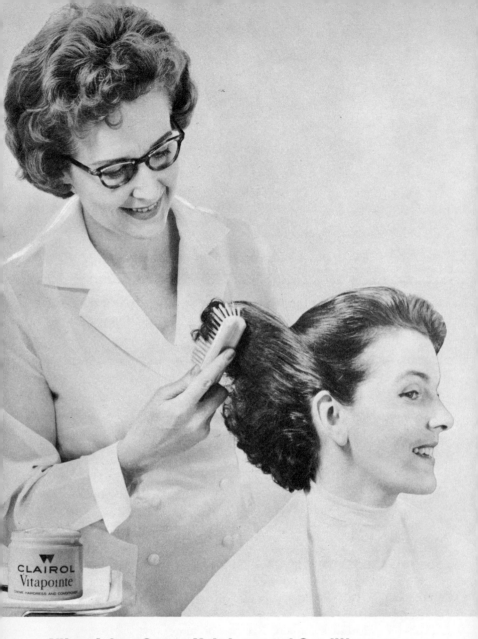

Vitapointe—Creme Hairdress and Conditioner

Vitapointe is the light, white, delicate creme hairdress that is made especially to dress a *woman's* hair. It is preferred by hairdressers everywhere because it adds the perfect finishing touch to all shades of natural, tinted or toned hair. Never greasy, the creme vanishes, gives hair greater beauty and sheen than any other hairdressing. Use Vitapointe after hair **has been** tinted, set and dried. It will not affect even the most delicate **Creme Toner** color.

172

Vitapointe

Hairdressers also prefer Vitapointe's light, white creme for use on gray hair. Unlike many other hairdressings, it does not turn hair yellow.

Apply by rubbing a tiny amount of Vitapointe on palms, then stroke lightly on hair. Or apply from palm to brush. Vitapointe is a "must" for the beautiful finishing touch to every coiffure.

Hair-So-New

Hair-So-New is used like an ordinary setting lotion, but it does so much more. It serves as a creme rinse, conditioning treatment and setting lotion—all in one. Hair-So-New actually combines chemically with the hair to give it more body, making it easier to set and helping the set to last longer. It eliminates snarls and tangles so hair is easier to comb. The conditioning action takes place under the dryer after you have set the hair, eliminating the heating cap used in most conditioning treatments.

Hair-So-New is recommended for hair that has been lightened, tinted or toned, sun-bleached or permanent-waved, but not for coated hair. Unlike most creme rinses, it does not strip color from hair. It restores elasticity, life and sheen to damaged hair.

HOW TO APPLY HAIR-SO-NEW AS A CONDITIONER

1. Use immediately after thorough shampoo. Be sure to rinse *all* the soap from the hair.

2. Wrap a towel around the patron's head for a few seconds to remove excess moisture.

3. Apply Hair-So-New from its push-button dispenser bottle on the ends of the hair first, then on the crown of the head, using just enough to give a smooth, silky feeling.*

4. Run a comb through the hair distributing the lotion throughout.

5. Do not rinse. Hair-So-New remains on hair and acts as your setting lotion.

6. Set and dry the hair as usual. The conditioning action takes place under the dryer.

*Be careful to avoid the delicate orbital areas as well as mouth and nose.

CHAPTER 18

CLAIR-FILL,
THE COLOR-BUILDER FOR
OVER-POROUS HAIR

EVERY haircolorist, no matter how skillful, runs into serious coloring problems when hair is over-porous. To fill a crying need for the solution of these difficulties, Clairol Research has developed CLAIR-FILL, a new filler concept.

Clair-Fill

This perfected filler, rich and creamy in consistency, comes in a wide range of colors. Clair-Fill is a *color-builder* . . . its function is to build color on damaged hair and make possible equal color-take on both over-porous and normal areas for even tone from roots to ends.

Wide Clair-Fill Color Range

There are seven Clair-Fill shades. They are:

1. Pale Gold   4. Brown   7. Platinum
2. Gold   5. Pink-Red
3. Brilliant Gold   6. Red

The first six of these shades may be intermixed to create any shade you need for a color base. Do not mix #7 Platinum with other Clair-Fill shades.

CLAIR-FILL COLOR SELECTOR

FOR OVER-LIGHTENED
AND OVER-POROUS HAIR

Key To Color Selection

Please note that the Clair-Fill colors are grouped by **shade classification**:

#1, #2 and #4 are to be used for Blonde and Brown shades

#3, #5 and #6 are to be used for the Red or Warm shades

#7 is to be used with Light Blonde toners (with blue or purple base) as well as a drabber to eliminate excess "yellow" from pre-lightened hair.

FOR BLONDE AND BROWN SHADES

CLAIR-FILL COLOR	MISS CLAIROL	CREME TONER
Pale Gold #1	Flaxen Blonde Topaz	9A Towhead Extra-Lite A Extra-Lite Silver 　　Blonde Silver Smoke Silver Blu Extra-Lite Platinum Silver Platinum Smoke Platinum Ivory Chiffon White Beige Platinum Beige Champagne Ice Champagne Parfait Champagne Sherbet
Gold #2 (Medium Gold)	Golden Apricot	Moonbeam Blonde Extra-Lite B Honey Chiffon Buttercup Beige Silver Beige
Brown #4	Moongold Chestnut Brown Coffee Brown Sable Brown	10 B Sandy Blonde Champagne Toast

CLAIR-FILL COLOR SELECTOR

FOR OVER-LIGHTENED
AND OVER-POROUS HAIR

FOR RED OR WARM SHADES

CLAIR-FILL COLOR	MISS CLAIROL OR RED FASHION COLOR	CREME TONER OR RED FASHION COLOR*
Brilliant Gold #3 (red gold)	Sun Bronze Sun Silver	Rose Beige Peach Chiffon Strawberry Blonde Sun Silver*
Pink-Red #5	Sparkling Sherry Red Ginger Cherry Silver	Pink Chiffon Cherry Silver*
Red #6 (orange red)	Flame Coppertone Fire Silver Pink Silver	Fire Silver* Pink Silver* *When the Red Fashion Colors are used as toners on pre-lightened hair.

PLATINUM #7

PLATINUM #7 FOR SILVER AND PLATINUM TONERS	PLATINUM #7—SPECIAL USE FOR DRABBING TO ELIMINATE EXCESS YELLOW
White Beige Champagne Ice Platinum Beige Extra-Lite Silver Blonde Silver Smoke Silver Blu Extra-Lite Platinum Silver Platinum Smoke Platinum	Extra-Lite Silver Blonde Silver Smoke Silver Blu Extra-Lite Platinum Silver Platinum Smoke Platinum White Beige Champagne Ice Platinum Beige (#7 may be used with all other Creme Toner shades if need arises.)

The Two Degrees of Porosity

In order to understand porosity, remember porosity means the condition of hair that makes it more receptive to the absorption of a tint.

You should recognize that there are *two* degrees of porosity:

1. *Desirable* porosity which permits the tint or toning mixture to penetrate satisfactorily. (Sometimes the porosity begins to go slightly beyond the desirable amount. This is noted by the color going a little too dark. It is remedied by addition of shampoo to the tint before applying to these areas.)

2. *Troublesome porosity*—a condition where the hair has become so over-porous the following problems result which you can solve with Clair-Fill correction. They are:

Hair doesn't hold color at all	**Off-color results**
Faded ends	**Color streaking**
Uneven color	**Poor tint-backs**

These problems occur during various stages of troublesome porosity:

    a. *In the early stages* the shade finishes too drab, off-color or incomplete looking. Or, ends do not hold sufficient color, color is too weak or too light.

    b. *In the extreme stages* hair has been so damaged it holds very little color or does not hold color at all.

Clair-Fill Simple To Use

Generally, there are two methods of using Clair-Fill to overcome these problems. When the problem is in the early stages, Clair-Fill is mixed with the tint or toner. When the problem is severe as in the extreme stages, use Clair-Fill before you tint or tone.

HOW TO USE CLAIR-FILL IN EARLY STAGES OF TROUBLESOME POROSITY

Note that Clair-Fill is simply *added* to the tint or toner mixture.

1. Retouch the new growth area in the usual way.

2. When roots have developed sufficiently add 1 oz. Clair-Fill (use the color chart for selection) to the balance of tint or toner and apply throughout.

3. Develop 5 minutes and start strand testing.

4. When the Strand Test indicates the color is even throughout, rinse and shampoo.

HOW TO USE CLAIR-FILL IN THE EXTREME STAGES OF TROUBLESOME POROSITY

To either correct or greatly improve problems where hair has been badly damaged, Clair-Fill should be applied to the "problem" areas *before* application of tint or toner.

1. Apply Clair-Fill selected to porous areas and wait 20 minutes.

2. Test a single strand of hair by rinsing with warm water and towel-dry.

3. If Strand Test shows color is holding, rinse. Towel dry hair if a toner is to be applied. Dry under dryer if Miss Clairol is to be applied.

4. Then proceed with tint or toner in the usual manner.

Color still weak? Then do not rinse Clair-Fill from the hair. Merely towel-dry excess and proceed with tint or toner as usual.

SPECIAL NOTES

1. If the corrective treatment still does not even the color out sufficiently, the next time follow the same procedure using a deeper Clair-Fill color in the same category in which you are working. For instance, if #1 Pale Gold is too weak, try #2 Gold, and if necessary, go to #4 Brown.

2. If the Clair-Fill shade chosen left too much color on the hair, the next time select the next lightest shade or mix it with a lighter shade.

3. Occasionally, if the results show a lack of warm or red highlights, a small amount of #3, #5 or #6 may be added to the Clair-Fill shade being used.

4. For less porous areas, dilute the Clair-Fill shade with equal parts of water.

5. When the haircolor has been evened out and once again wearing well (usually after the second or third corrective treatment), the use of Clair-Fill should be discontinued.

STRAND TEST

If you are in doubt as to the Clair-Fill shade to use for the corrective treatment make a Strand Test first.

    a. *For the early stages of porosity.* Mix a small amount of your tint or toner with the Clair-Fill shade and apply to a single strand. Develop for 10 minutes and start strand testing for results. If the shade is developing in the proper tone, use this mixture for the entire treatment.

    b. *For the extreme stages of porosity.* Apply the Clair-Fill shade to the problem area, wait 10 minutes, then Strand Test. If the ends are beginning to hold the Clair-Fill shade in the proper tone then proceed with the entire treatment.

SPECIAL USES OF CLAIR-FILL
IN SILVER AND PLATINUM TONING

When toning with the platinum and silver shades in the extreme stages of porosity, it is often necessary to use two Clair-Fill shades as follows:

1. Apply one of the blonde Clair-Fill shades to the "overlightened" ends first. Use the shade that will even to a yellow or pale yellow base best.

2. Apply the Platinum or Silver toner to the roots in the usual way.

3. Now add 1 oz. of #7 Platinum to the remaining toner mixture and apply throughout.

4. Develop 5 minutes and Strand Test. Continue strand testing until the color evens throughout.

5. Rinse and shampoo.

SPECIAL USE OF PLATINUM #7 AS A DRABBER IN TONING

To do successful toning the hair must be *lightened to the proper* stage, as well as made *sufficiently porous.* Sometimes too much brassy yellow or gold still remains in the hair. A "temporary" corrective treatment can be given with the use of Clair-Fill #7 Platinum as follows no matter what toner will be used:

1. Saturate brassy gold areas with undiluted Clair-Fill Platinum #7. Wait 5 minutes and start strand testing.

2. Continue strand testing until yellow has been reduced sufficiently.

3. Rinse and towel-dry. Proceed with toning application.

CLAIR-FILL AS A COLOR FRESHENER BETWEEN RETOUCHES

When hair shade has faded between retouches, it may be brightened and freshened.

1. Select Clair-Fill shade for highlights desired from Clair-Fill Color Selector.

2. Mix 1 part Clair-Fill to 2 parts shampoo.

3. Apply as a soap cap. Wait 5 minutes, then Strand Test for color.

4. When Strand Test shows color-take is sufficient, rinse thoroughly.

CHAPTER 19

REMOVING
TINT

Sometimes it is necessary to remove tint from the hair in order to apply a new shade. There are three means of doing this:

1. A Clairol Remov-zit treatment.

2. Lightening with any Lady Clairol Creme Hair Lightener.

3. A Remov-zit treatment followed by a later application of a lightener.

The following factors will help you select the best method: the time the patron can spend; the condition of the hair; the degree of tint removal required to make the color change desired.

Lightening to Remove a Tint

This is the most popular method of removing tint because new color may be applied the same day. Usually a patron does not have sufficient time for the 24-hour waiting period necessary between a Remov-zit treatment and application of fresh tint. She desires a lighter color on her hair the same day.

For this purpose you may use any one of the following mixtures recommended for the patron's hair type:

1. When the hair needs to be lightened only a few shades, it can be done with Clairolite, Lady Clairol (without Lightening Booster) or Ultra-Blue mixture (without Protinator).

2. When an extreme change in color is required (for example, hair tinted Black Velvet or Sable Brown is to be lightened for application of Chestnut Brown), a stronger lightening mixture must be used to lift the color sufficiently. Use Lady Clairol with 1 or 2 envelopes of Lightening Booster or Ultra-Blue Lady Clairol with 1 or 2 envelopes of Protinator.

3. When hair already has too much tint and is strong and resistant, use Clairol Blue Lightening Powder Bleach or Ultra-Blue Lady Clairol and 3 envelopes of Protinator.

LIGHTENING APPLICATION TIPS

Mixing and application of lightener for removing a tint is done using the method described for virgin hair. (See Chapter 7.) Use the additional tips listed below to insure best results.

1. Using narrow fiber brush or applicator, apply mixture to darkest portions of hair first and allow to lighten a little before application to rest of tinted hair.

2. If regrowth is light enough and color is to be lifted from the shaft and ends only, confine the lightener only to the areas to be lightened. When regrowth must also be lightened, apply to this portion last since it requires much less time to reach shade desired.

3. Always make small partings for application.

4. Strand Test frequently. Time required for treatment will vary according to texture of hair and degree of lightening required.

5. It is usually unnecessary to lighten beyond the red-gold (fourth) stage unless an extreme color change is desired.

6. If a single lightening treatment does not lighten hair sufficiently, a second application may be given the following day. This is sometimes necessary when hair is resistant or over-tinted.

7. When hair is light enough after treatment, but too much red or gold remains, drabber may be used. This may be determined by a Preliminary Strand Test.

8. When a new shade is to be applied the same day, be sure hair is rinsed and shampooed thoroughly, then towel-dried before beginning coloring treatment.

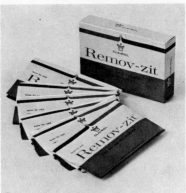

Remov-zit

If you prefer to use a color remover for penetrating tints and compound hennas, one of the most effective products is Clairol Remov-zit. It removes sufficient tint for application of fresh color but does not leave the hair pure white or lighten natural pigment. Therefore, it must not be used as a substitute for a lightener.

The number of treatments necessary to remove the desired amount of color depends upon the tint product used for coloring, its effect on the hair and the number of treatments hair has been given. Naturally, the more thoroughly the tint is impregnated in the hair shaft, the more treatments will be needed to lift it.

It may be noticed occasionally after a Remov-zit treatment that the color seems to have been removed unevenly. This can be caused by uneven application of the product. However, if brush application of Remov-zit has been made correctly and hair has been evenly saturated, you may assume that hair has been unevenly pre-lightened during some previous retouch treatment. Remov-zit, in this case, cannot make the color even. Lightening will be required on the dark portions, especially if the patron desires a lighter shade. If a darker shade is desired, no lightening is necessary.

When you are giving a series of Remov-zit treatments, you may discontinue treatments when you find no noticeable change from one treatment to the next.

Preparation of Remov-zit

Remov-zit package consists of two powders packaged separately, one in a gold and one in a silver envelope. The steps in using them follow:

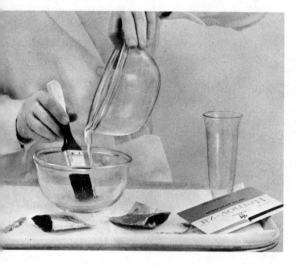

1. Dissolve the contents of the gold envelope in one ounce of hot or boiling water in a glass container. Do not use a metal container.

2. Dissolve the contents of the silver envelope in one ounce of hot or boiling water in a second glass container.

3. Now mix the two solutions together in a glass dish and stir.

In a Remov-zit treatment, the number of packages needed depends upon the quantity and length of the hair. Usually 2 or 3 of each package are required. It is important to remember that equal quantities of the contents of the gold and silver envelopes must be used. One ounce of hot water must be added for each individual package.

There are occasions when a further diluted solution should be used. Please refer to Case History No. 32 for information on this. But for maximum effectiveness in regular color removal, it is important to use the product full strength . . . 1 oz. of water for each package.

Application of Remov-zit

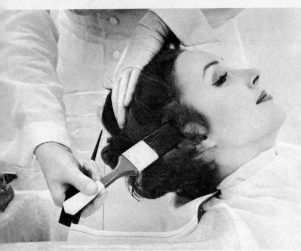

1. Do not brush hair the day treatment is given. Cover patron with a rubber cape or similar protection and seat at the shampoo basin. Place a towel between the patron and the shampoo board or sink. This towel will absorb any excess drippings that flow off the hair. No pre-shampoo is necessary.

2. Before application is started, check temperature of mixture to be certain it cannot burn patron's scalp or cause discomfort.

3. Apply the Remov-zit with a swab or brush. A small paint brush is best. Apply to the portions of hair which are to be decolorized.

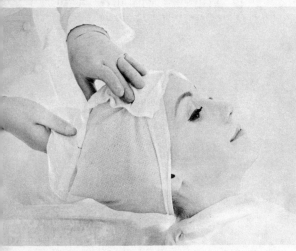

4. Pile the hair on top of the head. Hair must be saturated until it will not absorb any more moisture.

5. Wrap damp towel that has been used to catch drippings around head. A dry towel will absorb the tint remover.

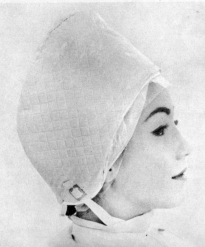

6. Place the patron under a steamer or heating cap for 30 minutes with the towel around head. The heat will hasten the action.

7. Rinse the hair with clear, warm water after 30 minutes. Do not use hot water.

184

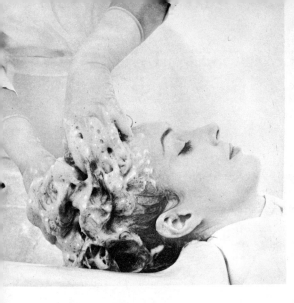

8. Shampoo thoroughly with Clairol Green Shampoo.

9. Give a very thorough final rinse with warm water. This final rinse is necessary to stop the action. It will, at the same time, remove a great deal of the odor which results from this type of treatment. Odor may be minimized by rinsing hair with a solution of a few drops of concentrated oil of lavender in a pint of water.

24-HOUR WAITING PERIOD

Twenty-four hours should elapse between the application of Remov-zit and the use of any tints, lighteners, pomades, lacquers, clips, bobby pins or wave lotions. This allows time for the maximum action of the tint remover. If less time is taken, it is possible for the hair to darken and sometimes revert to the color it was before the Remov-zit treatment. This necessitates starting the treatment over again.

When a series of Remov-zit treatments is given, it is preferable to space them a few days apart. On the other hand, Remov-zit can follow immediately after Metalex or other treatments.

Coloring After a Tint Remover Treatment

Hair treated with a tint remover will, in some cases, be quite porous and take coloring more easily. Because of ·this, when tinting after a tint removing treatment, it may be necessary to use a shade lighter than the final color desired, except when using Miss Clairol which has its own lightening action. On the other hand, some hair becomes resistant to color because of its natural texture. In this case, the tint has to be left on for a longer period and may need pre-lightening, especially if a shampoo tint will be used.

These factors should be determined by a Preliminary Strand Test. If, during the test, the strand quickly becomes a deeper color or goes black, this indicates that a longer waiting period is necessary before applying the tint or lightener.

If you know in advance that a patron is planning a color change requiring removal of the present tint shade, it is well to give several treatments of Metalex or **condition*** first. This will keep the hair in the best possible condition. (See Chapter 16.)

185

PROFESSIONAL
CASE HISTORIES
INDEX

On the following pages, 124 Professional Case Histories analyze problems brought to Clairol by hairdressers from all over the country. We hope you will find in these histories answers to your own questions.

If you have any problems which they do not answer, remember to write or call your local Clairol representative or the Clairol Institute of Haircoloring.

PROFESSIONAL

CASE

HISTORIES

All Blonding

1. ELIMINATING GOLD SPOTS IN ASH, SILVER AND PLATINUM BLONDING

PROBLEM: In Ash, Silver or Platinum Blonding uneven shades are liable to develop because of gold spots which have not been eliminated from the pre-lightened hair.

CAUSE: This can be caused either by uneven application of the lightener or by the fact that the natural pigmentation is distributed unevenly and requires spot lightening.

SOLUTION: Spot lightening of the remaining gold tones is the preferred solution. However, gold tones may be helped by using Silver or Smoke Platinum Salon Formula colors. Either of these colors should be applied to the gold spots only and allowed to develop until the gold is almost eliminated. Without shampooing the head, apply the selected color to the entire head in the regular manner. Or apply Clair-Fill #7 Platinum to these gold areas before application of the toner.

2. QUICK SPOT TONING

PROBLEM: In Ash, Silver or Platinum Blonding gold spots remain after toning.

CAUSE: Hair has been insufficiently pre-lightened on these areas.

SOLUTION: If there is insufficient time for further lightening or toning, these gold areas can be quickly eliminated temporarily by applying Come Alive Gray Silver Diamond. Mix a small amount of Silver Diamond with three times as much water. First make a Strand Test. If test indicates further dilution or concentration is necessary, make the needed adjustment and proceed to cover all gold areas. Or apply Clair-Fill #7 Platinum.

3. IN-BETWEEN TONING TREATMENT FOR SILVER OR ASH BLONDE HAIR

PROBLEM: Due to over-exposure to sun, excessive use of lacquer, improper shampoo, etc., toner has faded, but patron is not ready for a complete retouch.

SOLUTION: As an in-between toning treatment, the faded look can be avoided by applying Come Alive Gray after the weekly shampoo. For

191

toning light, delicate shades use White Sapphire; for medium shades, Silver Diamond; for darker shades use Black Pearl. In all cases take a Strand Test to determine the correct dilution. On very light, delicate shades, Clair-Fill #7 Platinum may be used.

4. UNEVEN TONING—TOO MUCH SILVER

PROBLEM: While Silver Blonding, too much silver or blue may develop on the hairline or temples.

CAUSE: This portion is over-lightened and has become over-porous. It may also be caused by slow application.

SOLUTION: When this occurs, the silver can be lifted quickly in one of the following ways:

1. Apply Strawberry Blonde Salon Formula without developer to the over-silvered area. Test every few minutes. When the excess has been lifted, rinse immediately.

2. Apply a mixture of one part Miss Clairol Sun Bronze and two parts developer. Test every few minutes. When excess has been lifted, rinse immediately.

3. Apply Clair-Fill Gold or Brilliant Gold over the silvered areas.

5. OVER-SILVERED HAIR

PROBLEM: In Silver Blonding hair may be so highly lightened that even diluted silver tints may give too much color and go too silver.

CAUSE: This may be caused by over-lightening, by over-porosity, by over-exposure to the sun or by a new permanent wave.

SOLUTION: Apply Clair-Fill first to the over-porous areas before application of tint. Or add Clair-Fill to the soap cap. To prevent over-silvered condition in future treatments mix 1¾ oz. Extra Lite Silver Blonde (Salon Formula) or Extra Lite Platinum (Salon Formula) with ¼ oz. Strawberry Blonde or Buttercup Beige and 2¼ oz. developer. Apply in the usual manner.

6. OVER-SILVERED HAIR—TOO BLUE

PROBLEM: Hair takes on too much blue tone during silvering process.

CAUSE: This may be caused by any of the following:

1. Slow application.

2. Too long a development period.

3. Improper color selection.

4. Too porous hair because of over-lightening.

SOLUTION: This may be corrected by any of the following methods:

1. If blue is too deep, apply Strawberry Blonde Salon Formula without developer in the same manner. Make frequent tests for color.

2. If blue is too deep, apply one part Miss Clairol Sun Bronze with two parts of developer. Test frequently. When excess is lifted, rinse immediately. Give Metalex treatments.

3. If hair is only slightly too blue, apply Buttercup Beige, and as soon as blue has disappeared, rinse immediately.

4. Apply Clair-Fill to the over-porous area to reduce the blue.

7. CONDITIONING DURING RETOUCH WHILE SILVER BLONDING

PROBLEM: Reconditioning the same day may leave the scalp sensitive to lightening and toning.

CAUSE: Reconditioning would require shampooing which is not recommended before lightening.

SOLUTION: Apply lightening mixture to the root area. Immediately after application of the lightener apply **condition*** to the rest of the hair strand. When the roots are lightened sufficiently, rinse and proceed with treatment.

8. SILVER BLONDING ON UNEVEN GRAY HAIR

PROBLEM: In Silver Blonding on gray hair the hair may be completely gray in front and only streaked with gray in back. The resulting Silver Blonde shade may be uneven.

CAUSE: Uneven pigmentation. White in front or yellow or brassy in back as a result of lightening.

SOLUTION: Use either of the following methods:

1. Use a Silver color on the back section only and an Ash Blonde color in the front. If the Ash Blonde is not quite silver enough, add to it a small quantity of the tint used in the back. If this method is used, the hair should finish with an even shade throughout.

2. Apply Clair-Fill to the white area to give it a pale gold base to approximate the color that is lacking. Then proceed with the Silver toner as usual.

9. SILVER BLONDING SALT-AND-PEPPER HAIR

PROBLEM: In applying Silver or Platinum colors to white and gray— "salt-and-pepper"—hair, there may be a tendency for the white hair to turn blue or purple.

CAUSE: White, being completely devoid of pigment, will naturally take on the color of the tint in the bottle. These tints have blue and purple tones because they are made to be used on yellow hair, not white.

SOLUTION: There are several methods:

1. Apply Clair-Fill Pale Gold, Gold or Brilliant Gold to the white areas. Or after applying tint to the back areas, to your remaining tint mixture add Clair-Fill Pale Gold, Gold or Brilliant Gold and apply this mixture to the white areas.

2. Add an Ash, Neutral or Beige to the Silver or Platinum tone which will add some color base to the white hair. The percentage of each shade in the mixture used depends entirely upon the amount of gray in the hair. The amount of the base color used should increase in proportion to the amount of gray existing in the hair. A Strand Test should be given to determine the exact proportions of Silver or Platinum and base color to be used.

75% gray—3 parts base shade to 1 part Silver or Platinum.

50% gray—Equal parts of Ash Blonde and Silver or Platinum.

25% gray—2 to 3 parts of Silver or Platinum to 1 part of Ash Blonde.

Coated Hair
10. COATED HAIR—RINSES

PROBLEM: Customer is about to receive a permanent wave, but the hair is heavily coated and excessively dry.

CAUSE: Hair has been exposed to too many hair rinses.

SOLUTION: To insure a better wave and avoid the possibility of discoloration, the coating should be stripped off. This can be done with a Metalex treatment. The hair is saturated with the Metalex, then heated for 30 minutes with either a heating cap or a steamer. The coating will then be removed, and the hair will be reconditioned, leaving it in a workable condition. If the coating is excessively heavy, several treatments may be needed.

11. COATED HAIR—CRAYONS

PROBLEM: Gray hair treated with a hair crayon is hard to cover.

CAUSE: The hair crayon coats the hair and makes it difficult for the color to penetrate unless the hair is first shampooed.

SOLUTION: In order to save time and energy, the shampoo can be avoided with the use of Miss Clairol. Apply the Miss Clairol mixture to be used throughout the head, starting with portion covered with crayon. As soon as entire application is finished, wipe off crayon-covered area with towel. Reapply Miss Clairol mixture to cleansed area.

12. COATED HAIR—METALLIC DYE OR METALLIC HAIR RESTORER

PROBLEM: Hair does not permanent wave or tint successfully because customer has previously used a metallic dye or hair restorer.

CAUSE: Metallic dyes coat the hair and therefore must be removed before a permanent wave, tint or lightener is applied. If this is not done, discoloration (purple, green or black) or breakage will result.

SOLUTION: Give a series of Metalex treatments. When sufficient coating has been removed and hair feels normal, give a Strand Test with either the coloring mixture or the lightener, or a test curl for the permanent wave. If the results are satisfactory, you may continue with your tint, lightener or permanent-wave treatment. If the results are not satisfactory, that means metallic salts still remain in the hair and more Metalex treatments should be given. The number of treatments that may be needed depends upon the degree of coating.

13. COATED HAIR—COMPOUND HENNA

PROBLEM: Permanent wave, tint or lightener over compound henna causes hair to discolor or break.

CAUSE: Compound henna coats hair, making successful permanent waving, lightening or tinting impossible.

SOLUTION: Give series of Metalex treatments. Then take Strand Test for color or a test curl for the permanent wave. If the strand turns green or gets hot, the hair is still excessively coated and stained and must be treated intermittently with Metalex and Remov-zit. (Remember, the 24-hour waiting period after the use of the Remov-zit applies here, too.) Repeat the Strand Test or test curl. If unsatisfactory, continue Metalex treatments.

14. COATED HAIR—TEMPORARY STREAKS

PROBLEM: Patron has used temporary powders for streak effects. These make tinting difficult or cause discoloration.

CAUSE: Powders or greases used for this purpose are temporary colors and obtain their effect by coating the hair. This interferes with the penetration of a tint or lightener.

SOLUTION: Remove the coloring before applying tint or lightener. A shampoo will remove the coloring if it has only been used once or twice. However, if it has been used over a period of time, use a Metalex treatment as shampooing will not remove the coloring. Metalex should also be used if discoloration has resulted.

15. COATED HAIR—TEMPORARY COLORING

PROBLEM: Patron has coated hair from the use of hair sprays that contain temporary coloring. This coating makes tinting difficult and often causes discoloration.

CAUSE: These products interfere with the penetration of tints.

SOLUTION: Use Metalex treatment. One treatment is usually sufficient.

16. TINTING OVER COATED HAIR CERTIFIED RINSES

PROBLEM: Hair is so badly coated that it is difficult to lighten or tint.

CAUSE: This is something that often happens when certified rinses have been used on a patron's hair and have been doubled and tripled in strength in order to obtain some coverage of gray.

SOLUTION: Coating must be removed. This may be done with one or two Metalex treatments.

17. HENNA PACK INTERFERES WITH PERMANENT WAVING

PROBLEM: Sometimes the coating left after a henna pack interferes with permanent waving.

CAUSE: Many applications of henna have coated hair heavily.

SOLUTION: Give a Metalex treatment to remove the coating. A series of treatments may be necessary.

18. HENNA PACK—TOO TIME CONSUMING

PROBLEM: Henna pack may be objected to because applications are too time consuming.

CAUSE: If hair is very dark, henna is not very effective.

SOLUTION: Henna packs can be adequately substituted for by using Miss Clairol Red Ginger. Similar effect can be produced in from 5 to 10 minutes.

WARNING: Do not use Red Ginger over henna of the compound type until it is removed. Where doubt exists, give a Strand Test for compound henna.

19. TEST FOR METALLIC SALTS (The "1-20" Test)

PROBLEM: Many times a patron coming for a permanent wave or hair-color treatment either cannot or will not tell what preparations she has previously used on her hair. If metallic compounds have been used, trouble may result in the form of breakage or discoloration. Thus it is necessary to test to determine if metallic compounds have been used.

SOLUTION: Hair that has been treated with either a hair restorer, metallic dye or compound henna will appear to be dull, with no highlights. Each hair is solidly colored, without the shading found in natural pigmented hair. Hair is heavy with coating, generally harsh or brittle. These colorings usually fade into unnatural shades. The dyes that contain lead turn purple. Those containing silver turn green. Those containing copper turn red. Following is the test for Metallic Salts:

THE "1-20" TEST

The Test for Metallic Salts is usually called the "1-20" test.

1. Mix in a glass container 1 oz. of 20-vol. peroxide and 20 drops of ammonia 28%.

2. Cut a piece of hair from the area on the patron's head which has been most frequently exposed to the coloring.

3. Bind with scotch tape and immerse in the above solution for 30 minutes. Then remove from dish and let stand for 24 hours.

Most of these products contain lead, silver or copper salts. Here are the reactions to look for:

Lead—Hair will change color immediately. It often turns much lighter very rapidly.

Silver—No reaction whatsoever at end of half hour. A peroxide and ammonia solution cannot lighten this base because it cannot penetrate, while a strand with no artificial coloring or a penetrating tint will lighten to some degree.

Copper—Solution will start to boil within a few minutes. Strand feels hot. It throws off a very disagreeable odor. After a few minutes, the hair will pull apart easily.

If any of these conditions is evident, the metallic coating must be removed before hair can be successfully colored or permanented.

In all cases, after the coating has been removed, the strand should be checked again in 24 hours by stretching for breakage. If breakage occurs, this means that the hair is so badly damaged that it must first be reconditioned before the haircoloring can be applied. In some cases damage may be so great a short haircut is advisable.

Discoloration

20. GREEN DISCOLORATION— RINSE ON LIGHTENED HAIR

PROBLEM: Patron's hair has green discoloration.

CAUSE: This may be caused by the use of a drab rinse as a toner over lightened hair which is too yellow, too gold or too porous. The gold combines with the bluish color of the rinse to give a green shade.

SOLUTION: In future, avoid the use of rinse. Use Clair-Fill #7 Platinum or Come Alive Gray White Sapphire. To correct existing problem use one of the following methods:

1. Apply either Pink-Red or Red Clair-Fill to the green areas to eliminate the green.

2. Apply Strawberry Blonde Salon Formula without developer or a mixture of 1 part Miss Clairol Sun Bronze and 2 parts developer. Apply

to the green areas only. In extreme cases of green discoloration it is advisable to follow with a Metalex treatment on this type of hair.

21. GREEN DISCOLORATION—PERMANENT WAVE OVER HAIR WITH BLUE RINSE

PROBLEM: A permanent wave is given on yellowed white hair that has previously been given blue rinses. The hair turns green.

CAUSE: Blue rinse should have been removed before the permanent wave was given. Metalex should have been used for this.

SOLUTION: There are several ways to solve this problem:

1. Give a Metalex treatment. If this does not remove color sufficiently, use Remov-zit.

2. When Remov-zit is used, it is not always necessary to use a heating cap after the Remov-zit has been applied. Test for color as soon as the Remov-zit has been applied. If color has been lifted sufficiently, rinse and shampoo immediately. If it hasn't, use a heating cap. Remember, nothing else should be applied to the hair within 24 hours.

3. Sometimes an application of Clair-Fill in Brilliant Gold, Pink-Red or Red will remove the green. Strand Test to determine which Clair-Fill color to use.

22. GREEN DISCOLORATION—PERMANENT WAVE OVER COMPOUND HENNA

PROBLEM: Hair turns green after permanent wave.

CAUSE: This is an example of what may happen if metallic coatings are not removed before permanent waving. Customer may henna her hair at home. Not knowing that there are two types of henna, pure and compound, she may lead you to believe that it is the pure vegetable type. Since compound henna contains metallic salts, the permanent-wave solution will turn the hair green if that is what has been used.

SOLUTION: First give a Metalex treatment to remove the coating. Then use Remov-zit to remove the discoloration. You may give the Remov-zit treatment immediately after the Metalex treatment, but you must wait 24 hours after the Remov-zit treatment before any further treatments can be given to the hair. The number of treatments needed depends upon the degree of coating and staining. When you feel that the hair has reacted sufficiently, take a Strand Test for color. If any of the compound remains, the hair will again turn green indicating that the treatment should be continued. When the Strand Test has been satisfactory, proceed with the color treatment. Do not use lightener to correct this particular problem since developer will only bring up more of the greenish cast. Of course, after the problem has been corrected, lighteners may be used.

23. GREEN DISCOLORATION—CHLORINATED WATER

PROBLEM: Blonde hair takes on a greenish cast after patron has been swimming in a pool.

CAUSE: Too much chlorine in the water.

SOLUTION: If hair has been lightened, use Strawberry Blonde Salon Formula without developer, Miss Clairol Sun Bronze with two or three parts of Clairoxide or Clair-Fill Brilliant Gold. (In severe cases choose Pink-Red or Red Clair-Fill.) If hair is natural blonde correct it with Clair-Fill Brilliant Gold, Pink-Red, or Red. In serious cases of either give a Metalex treatment first, then a corrective. Advise your customer to wear a bathing cap in the future.

24. GREEN DISCOLORATION—BLUE RINSE ON YELLOWED WHITE HAIR

PROBLEM: Blue rinse is applied to white hair which has yellowed from an acid condition. Hair turns green.

CAUSE: Combination of blue rinse over yellow gives a green shade.

SOLUTION: Use Metalex to remove the green discoloration. Do not use coloring or lighteners to correct this condition. They will lighten the hair which has not been affected, and a new problem will be created. If the problem is serious enough, use several Metalex treatments. In extreme cases diluted Remov-zit will be necessary.

25. BLUE DISCOLORATION—ERMINE OR STARLIGHT

PROBLEM: Hair turns blue after using Miss Clairol Ermine or Starlight on lightened hair.

CAUSE: This can be caused by the hair's having been over-lightened. It then becomes too porous and takes on too much color, thus turning blue.

SOLUTION: There are two methods to solve this problem:

1. Give a Metalex treatment to lift the excess blue. If some blue still remains, use either Strawberry Blonde Salon Formula without developer or Miss Clairol Sun Bronze with two or three parts of developer. If some blue still remains, give another Metalex treatment. In extreme cases highly diluted Remov-zit will remove this discoloration.

2. An application of Clair-Fill in Brilliant Gold, Pink-Red or Red will lift the blue. Strand Test to determine which filler shade will do the best job.

26. GRAY HAIR—ATTEMPTED PERMANENT BLUING TREATMENT

PROBLEM: Attempt has been made to give a permanent bluing treatment to gray hair of the salt-and-pepper type. Permanent discoloration results with dark hair going light and white hair growing brownish.

CAUSE: A permanent bluing effect cannot be given successfully because blue is unstable and fades rapidly, and the developer has a lightening action on the pigment of the hair.

SOLUTION: Never give a treatment of this type. If the treatment has been given, the best that can be done is to give a Metalex treatment to lift the blue and some of the brown. Then cover up by using Come Alive Gray or a Silk & Silver treatment. Do not attempt to correct this by additional lightening.

27. DISCOLORATION—COLORED BLEACHES

PROBLEM: Patron's hair becomes discolored during the use of colored oil bleach.

CAUSE: This is generally caused by frequently overlapping the colored bleach on a portion previously lightened. This area then becomes too porous and absorbs some of the color in the bleach. This condition may also be caused by a new permanent wave.

SOLUTION: First the discoloration must be removed. Specific solutions are discussed in case histories 28, 29, 32, 122.

Reconditioning treatments should be given in order to avoid this condition in the future. Metalex or **condition*** may be used. While the problem exists, discoloration may be avoided by applying **condition*** to the shaft to improve and protect it and diluting the colored bleach with an equal amount of Neutral Clairolite Bleach. When the hair is no longer too porous, you can go back to the original mixture.

28. GRAY DISCOLORATION—DRAB OIL BLEACH

PROBLEM: Gray stain caused by colored oil bleach.

CAUSE: This is caused by applying a drab bleach over over-lightened or badly permanent waved hair.

SOLUTION: Apply one of the following:

1. Clair-Fill Brilliant Gold, Pink-Red or Red.

2. Strawberry Blonde Salon Formula without developer applied to the grayish spots.

3. Gold Clairolite applied in the usual manner. Test frequently. When discoloration is lifted, shampoo immediately.

29. GREEN OR BLUE DISCOLORATION—SILVER BLEACH

PROBLEM: Green or blue stain caused by colored oil bleach.

CAUSE: This is caused by applying a silver bleach over over-lightened or badly permanent waved hair.

SOLUTION: Apply any of the following solutions to the discolored area:

1. Clair-Fill, using Brilliant Gold, Pink-Red or Red, depending on which color will make the correction most rapidly.

2. Strawberry Blonde Salon Formula without developer.

3. Miss Clairol Sun Bronze with two parts developer.

4. Gold Clairolite plus a few drops of Red Clairolite applied in the usual manner. Test frequently. When the green has been lifted, shampoo immediately.

30. DISCOLORATION—LIGHTENER OR TINT OVER PENETRATING RINSE

PROBLEM: Hair turns green on application of lightener or tint.

CAUSE: This happens when lighteners are applied over penetrating (aniline) rinses in drab shades. The lightener penetrates through the artificial coloring but does not remove it enough. As a result, the hair pigment is lightened blonde, but the rinse which remains gives a green effect.

SOLUTION: Give a Remov-zit treatment. In 24 hours take a color Strand Test. If the green has returned to some degree, it may be removed with the following mixture: 1 oz. Gold Clairolite, 2 oz. peroxide, with a few drops of Red Clairolite. This should be applied to the area with the greenish cast and tested very frequently. As soon as the green has been eliminated, apply the mixture to all discolored areas and allow to develop fully. If, however, the hair continues to take even more green, rinse the hair immediately and give another Remov-zit treatment. After the regular 24-hour waiting period, repeat the test. If the results are satisfactory, complete the treatment.

31. ORANGE OR PINK DISCOLORATION—UNDERDEVELOPMENT

PROBLEM: Hair takes on orange or pink tones after a penetrating color treatment in which a warm or red shade is used.

CAUSE: This orange or pink cast with a warm or red shade is caused by underdeveloped color. It may be due to any of the following reasons:

1. Weak developer.

2. Old tint.

3. Hair previously coated—tint could not penetrate.

4. Tint not left on long enough.

5. Too light a color selected for the amount of coloring required to blend with previous color given.

SOLUTION: Do not lighten. If your investigation shows that reason

1, 2, 3 or 4 has caused the underdeveloped color, prepare a new mixture of the same color, being careful that your developer and tint are fresh enough. Reapply the mixture to complete the color development. It is necessary, however, to test more frequently since the hair is already partially developed, and less development time will be needed for this application.

If reason 5 applies, select a darker color for the reapplication.

32. RED OR ORANGE DISCOLORATION—RED OIL BLEACH

PROBLEM: Red or orange stain caused by red colored oil bleach.

CAUSE: Red oil bleach applied over over-lightened or badly permanent waved hair.

SOLUTION: If the correction is made as soon as the staining occurs, it can be removed with Metalex. If the stain is of long standing, then lighten with Regular or Instant Whip Lady Clairol (no Booster). If the staining still remains, a highly diluted solution of Remov-zit should be used. (Use 3 oz. of water instead of 1, as called for in directions.) With Remov-zit, remember the 24-hour waiting period.

33. GREEN DISCOLORATION—UNDERDEVELOPMENT

PROBLEM: Hair takes on a greenish cast after a penetrating color treatment in a drab or gold color. This is not to be confused with the greenish color that is a result of compound and metallic salts.

CAUSE: This greenish cast with a drab shade is caused by underdeveloped color. It may be due to any of the following reasons:

1. Weak developer.

2. Old tint.

3. Hair previously coated—tint could not penetrate.

4. Tint not left on long enough.

5. Too light a color may have been selected for the amount of coloring required to blend with the color that had previously been applied to the hair.

SOLUTION: Do not lighten. If your investigation shows that reason 1, 2, 3 or 4 has caused the underdeveloped shade, prepare a new mixture of the same color, being careful that your developer and tint are fresh enough. Reapply the mixture to complete the color development. It is necessary, however, to test more frequently, since the hair is already partially developed, and less development time will be needed for this application.

If reason 5 applies, select a darker color for the reapplication.

34. PLATINUM OR SILVER TONER RESULTS IN BROWNISH CAST

PROBLEM: Sometimes during a Silver Blonde treatment the toner develops a brownish cast.

CAUSE: This is caused either because the tint is too old or the developer is too weak. The mixture could never reach the true shade. This could be avoided if it was observed during application.

SOLUTION: Work a diluted lightener through the hair in order to lift off the discoloration. Then shampoo, rinse and proceed with the usual method of application of toner mixture. Be sure to use fresh material.

Fading

35. TO MODIFY RED OR GOLD TONES IN TINTED, SUN-BLEACHED OR PERMANENT WAVED HAIR

PROBLEM: Red or gold tones have developed in tinted, sun-bleached or permanent waved hair.

CAUSE: Hair has been bleached by sun, new permanent or strong soap shampoos.

SOLUTION: Apply any one of the Come Alive Gray shades, testing dilution before complete application. On light, delicate shades you may use Clair-Fill #7 Platinum.

36. FADING COLOR

PROBLEM: Excessive amount of color lost during shampoos.

CAUSE: Detergents, soapless oil, sulphonated shampoos and medicated shampoos tend to strip color. Creme shampoos and creme rinses also strip color.

SOLUTION: Use or suggest new mild Clairol, the colorfast shampoo, Green for Tint and lasting rinse users. If a creme rinse is needed, dilute it greatly for the least possible amount of color stripping. Clairol Hair-So-New will remove snarls and tangles and recondition the hair at the same time without affecting the color.

Gray and White Hair

37. MAKING PARTIALLY GRAY HAIR COMPLETELY GRAY

PROBLEM: Patron has gray hair and wishes to become evenly gray, but she has a great deal of natural pigment.

CAUSE: Making hair grayer is sometimes desirable in order to make the hair a more even shade.

SOLUTION: All the dark pigment must first be lightened out then tinted with Smoke Platinum in Salon Formula. There is nothing on the market that will do this without lightening first. A rinse can be used but the results are not permanent.

38. TINTING GRAY HAIR—STREAKS

PROBLEM: Patron has gray hair only in the front of her head. The gray is in streaks. She wishes to color the gray without tinting entire head.

CAUSE: Color change is desired.

SOLUTION: There are two methods:

1. Select a tint closest to her natural color and apply to the gray portion only. As soon as the gray is colored to match her natural color, rinse the hair and shampoo.

2. Apply Loving Care.

39. YELLOW DISCOLORATION IN WHITE HAIR

PROBLEM: White hair may have a tendency to take on a yellow discoloration quite undesirable.

CAUSE: This may be caused by one of the following:

1. Excessive rinses.

2. Excessive heat from dryers or permanent waves.

3. Systemic condition.

SOLUTION: Determine which is the cause and use one of the following treatments:

1. Give a Silk & Silver treatment using shades #11 or #12.

2. Apply Clair-Fill #7 Platinum.

3. If the discoloration has been caused by excessive use of rinses, this will be evident by the harsh, coated texture of the hair. The color also has more of a yellow brown which is staining. The solution for this cause is a Metalex treatment.

4. In extreme cases staining and discoloration must be removed with a highly diluted solution of Remov-zit.

5. After removing coating and discoloration, hair may be made white with Come Alive Gray White Sapphire.

40. INSUFFICIENT COLOR—ADDITIONAL GRAY HAIR

PROBLEM: Patron has been having successful tint treatment for years but suddenly does not get sufficient color or depth of color.

CAUSE: The amount of the patron's gray hair may have increased. If this is the case, the same formula will no longer give the same shade.

SOLUTION: Select a color one or two shades deeper than the color used in the past. It is wise, however, to keep in mind that fact that the grayer a woman gets, the lighter it is advised to tint her hair.

41. PLATINUM HAIR

PROBLEM: Patron with dark hair wishes to have all coloring lightened out leaving her hair completely white or platinum. This cannot be done with lightener alone.

CAUSE: If lightener is counted upon to remove all pigments, breakage will occur. Therefore, a tint must be used.

SOLUTION: There are two methods for achieving platinum hair.

1. a. Use Ultra-Blue Lady Clairol with 2 Protinator Envelopes to lighten hair as light as possible, to pale yellow stage. If hair is strong, resistant, and in good condition, you may use 3 Protinator Envelopes.
b. Tint with Extra-Lite Platinum or White Beige in Salon Formula. Allow the tint to develop until all of the yellow has been drabbed out.

2. Lighten hair to almost white stage using Ultra-Blue Lady Clairol with 2 Protinator Envelopes or, on extremely dark resistant hair, use Blue Lightening Powder Bleach.
a. Tint with either Silver Smoke or Silver Blu (Salon Formula) or Miss Clairol Ermine. Allow the hair to drab as much as possible until it takes on at least a slight bluish cast.
b. Rinse, shampoo and towel dry.
c. Apply Metalex. Heat for 20 to 35 minutes with either steamer or heating cap. As soon as the blue has been lifted, shampoo again. The lightening lightens the hair. The blue drabs out the remaining color tones, and the Metalex lifts out the tint.

Hair Condition
42. DULL, GUMMY HAIR

PROBLEM: Hair tends to gum up after color treatments.

CAUSE: This may be due to hard water prevalent in many communities.

SOLUTION: Use Sylk in your shampoo, or give a Sylk Rinse after the hair has been shampooed. In very bad cases, it is necessary to give two Sylk Rinses to rid the hair of this gum.

43. RESISTANT HAIR

PROBLEM: Impossible to get 100% coverage on gray hair.

CAUSE: Hair is extremely resistant to color.

SOLUTION: Any of the following:

1. Since this type hair will not absorb color rapidly, the color has a tendency to be rejected and to roll down the strand of hair. One solution is to apply the tint lightly to the new growth the first time. As soon as the application is completed, go over the same areas again using a greater quantity of the same material. During the few minutes the original application is on, the cuticle layer will be softened, and the hair will become more receptive to the tint.

2. Add a few capfuls of Miss Clairol Black Velvet to the tint mixture. This gives a little more coloring value and thus insures better coverage.

3. Mix 2 oz. of the color selected with 1¾ oz. of Clairoxide or Pure White Creme Developer.

4. If any of the above methods fail, then hair should be pre-softened. Instead of using an oil bleach method, however, apply a regular mixture of Miss Clairol Topaz or Flaxen Blonde to the new growth. This method decreases the development time of the desired shade, because while softening the hair, it is also adding some color to the gray and white hair. If the Topaz or Flaxen Blonde is not applied too heavily, the hair need not be pre-shampooed. Selected color can be applied directly over it.

44. OVER-POROUS HAIR—DIFFICULT TO TINT OR PERMANENT WAVE

PROBLEM: Sometimes the hair is over-porous and has a tendency to grab too much color or too much of the permanent wave solution. This makes tinting or permanent wave treatments difficult to control.

CAUSE: Hair may become over-porous from over-lightening, improper permanent waving, sun-bleaching or improper tinting.

SOLUTION: Some of the porosity may be reduced by an application of Clairol **condition***. Shampoo hair, rinse thoroughly and towel dry. Apply a small quantity of **condition*** to the very porous areas and proceed with tint or permanent wave treatment.

45. OVER-POROUS HAIR—DIFFICULT TO TINT

PROBLEM: Sometimes the hair is over-porous with the result that there is no color-take or drab results.

CAUSE: Improper lightening, improper permanent waving, sun-bleaching or improper tinting.

SOLUTION: If colors are going drab or if there is little or no color-take, apply Clair-Fill. Some of the porosity may be reduced by an application of Clairol **condition***. Shampoo hair, rinse thoroughly and towel dry. Apply a small quantity of **condition*** to the very porous areas and proceed with the tint. If colors are going too dark, use **condition***.

Lightening
46. OVER-LIGHTENED SECTIONS OF HAIR

PROBLEM: Hair turns white in sections during lightening; consequently the sections will either go too drab or not hold color at all, and the toning will be uneven.

CAUSE: This is caused by over-lightening which is due to careless application or the over-lapping of too many lighteners. When this happens, too much of the gold tone is destroyed, and it must be artificially replaced for even results.

SOLUTION: After lightening hair in the usual manner, use one of the following procedures:

1. **Clair-Fill**

Apply Clair-Fill Pale Gold, Gold or Brilliant Gold (depending upon how much color is needed) before tinting or during retouch treatment.

2. **Strawberry Blonde**

a. Apply Strawberry Blonde Salon Formula without developer to all white or over-lightened areas. Apply strand by strand. If spots take too much color, gently rub off excess with a damp towel. (A damp towel is gentler on the hair until color evens itself out.)

b. Do not rinse hair, but apply toner directly in the usual manner.

3. **Buttercup Beige**

a. Apply Buttercup Beige mixed with equal amount of developer to the over-lightened areas.

b. Develop until the shade is even throughout. Then rinse, towel dry and apply the color desired.

47. INSUFFICIENT LIGHTENING WITH MISS CLAIROL

PROBLEM: Sometimes with Miss Clairol the color selected is satisfactory but the degree of lightening is insufficient.

CAUSE: Limited lightening action in color selected.

SOLUTION: Lightening action must be increased in either of the following ways:

1. Add from 2 capfuls to $\frac{1}{4}$ oz. Topaz or Flaxen Blonde.

2. Use double the normal amount of Clairoxide or Pure White Creme Developer. Coverage of gray will be weakened a bit in this case.

3. Add from $\frac{1}{8}$ to $\frac{1}{4}$ oz. Regular or Instant Whip Lady Clairol to regular Miss Clairol mixture. Add an additional amount of Clairoxide to allow for this.

48. LIGHTENING DARK OR RESISTANT HAIR

PROBLEM: Sometimes an attempt to lighten dark or resistant hair in the shortest possible time may cause abuse to the hair and abrasions and blisters to the scalp.

CAUSE: The amount of lightening the scalp can take is limited by the sensitivity of the individual being treated.

SOLUTION: The best way to prevent this is to keep the lightener from the scalp for the longest possible period of time. Starting 1 inch from the scalp, apply the lightener on entire strand (unless the ends are damaged, in which case omit the ends). The second application is applied directly from the scalp to the ends without shampooing between applications. Some of the lightener from the first application can, however, be wiped away with a towel, enabling second application to penetrate more quickly.

49. LIGHTENED HAIR BREAKAGE TEST

PROBLEM: Many times a patron who wishes a coloring treatment or permanent wave has lightened hair which is too dry, brittle or weak for proper work.

CAUSE: This may be caused by the fact that too many lightening treatments have been given without reconditioning. It may also be caused by overlapping of lighteners. This damages the hair.

SOLUTION: First it is necessary to determine how much damage has been done. A test can be made during shampoo or by wetting a strand with developer. If the hair feels gummy to the touch and can be easily pulled apart, it means that the hair is damaged and must be reconditioned or else breakage will occur during the coloring treatment or permanent wave.

Reconditioning can be done with a series of Metalex or **condition*** treatments.

50. BREAKAGE—OVER-LIGHTENING

PROBLEM: Breakage on highly lightened hair.

CAUSE: This can be caused by any of the following reasons:

1. Careless application of lighteners.

2. Too many retouches which overlap and cause damage.

3. Improper permanent wave.

4. Use of a lightener which is too strong.

5. Frequent pinning up of hair with bobby pins.

SOLUTION: Give series of Metalex or **condition*** treatments. Apply in the usual manner except when there is breakage. If there is breakage, simply rinse the Metalex out thoroughly, without shampooing.

51. RESISTANT HAIR—HARD TO LIGHTEN

PROBLEM: Hair is resistant and is very hard to lighten.

CAUSE: Texture of hair and/or overabundance of natural red pigment makes lightening difficult. Patron desires a very light toner.

SOLUTION: Use either of the following lighteners:

1. Apply Blue Lightening Powder Bleach.

2. Apply Ultra-Blue with 2 Protinator Envelopes. If hair is extremely resistant, use 3 Protinator Envelopes.

52. LIGHTENING VIRGIN HAIR— ROOTS APPEAR LIGHTER THAN ENDS

PROBLEM: Often when lightening virgin hair with a lightener or Miss Clairol, the roots appear to lighten more than the ends. This occurs especially when hair is being lightened a number of shades.

CAUSE: Body heat has a tendency to increase lightening action at the roots.

SOLUTION: If using Miss Clairol, use one of these methods in accordance with lightening action of color selected:

1. When going a few shades lighter, apply the tint throughout the hair except at the ends. Save a small quantity of the mixture; then add an extra portion of Clairoxide or Pure White Creme Developer to it before applying to the ends.

2. When going several shades lighter, apply the color throughout the hair except at the roots. Wait until the hair has begun to lighten. Then apply to the roots. If a lightener is used, keep mixture from roots until the last.

53. LIGHTENING FOLLOWING TINT REMOVER TREATMENT (AFTER 24 HOURS)

PROBLEM: Lightener is applied the required 24 hours after the tint remover treatment. In spite of this, hair goes very dark or black.

CAUSE: This may be caused by one of two things:

1. Insufficient rinsing of tint remover after treatment.

2. Insufficient number of tint remover treatments given.

In both cases, color remains in the hair and resets itself when lightener is applied.

SOLUTION: Rinse lightener from the hair immediately. Reapply tint remover in the regular manner. Wait from 24 to 48 hours. Then give a single color Strand Test to predetermine the results. If the color again is dark, the tint remover treatments must be continued. This could have been avoided in the first place if single Strand Tests were given instead of applying lightener to the whole head at once.

Permanent Waving

54. OVER-POROUS HAIR—DIFFICULT TO PERMANENT WAVE

PROBLEM: Sometimes the hair is over-porous and has a tendency to grab too much of the permanent waving solution, making the application difficult to control.

CAUSE: Hair may become over-porous from over-lightening, improper permanent waving, sun-bleaching or improper tinting.

SOLUTION: Use any of the following:

1. Recondition the hair by giving one or several Metalex treatments.

2. Give a **condition*** treatment just before the permanent.

3. Apply a thin application of **condition*** to the porous areas just before applying the permanent waving solution.

55. PERMANENT WAVE LEAVES HAIR TOO LIGHT

PROBLEM: After a new permanent wave, the hair may appear too light and the patron may object to this.

CAUSE: Permanent waving solutions have a tendency to lighten hair.

SOLUTION: Use either Miss Clairol or Salon Formula as a shampoo cap. With Miss Clairol use the exact color desired, mixing one part color to one part developer. With Salon Formula use the exact color desired, mixing one part color and one part developer and one part shampoo. Test immediately and shampoo. The complete treatment should take no more than 5 minutes. Or, use Loving Care in the shade closest to the natural color.

56. COLORING OVER NEW PERMANENT

PROBLEM: Sometimes dark ends and streaks result when tinting the hair immediately after having given a new permanent wave.

CAUSE: A permanent wave may leave the hair excessively porous, causing too much color to be absorbed.

SOLUTION: To correct this condition, apply lightener to the streaked portions and dark ends. It may also be corrected with Miss Clairol using a mixture of 1 oz. Topaz or Flaxen Blonde and $1/2$ oz. Ermine and 3 oz. developer. You may avoid this condition by protecting the more porous regions before applying the tint by using Clairol **condition*.**

57. PERMANENT WAVING OVER-LIGHTENED HAIR

PROBLEM: Over-lightened hair is difficult to permanent wave. Breakage may result.

CAUSE: Over-lightening destroys elasticity of hair.

SOLUTION: Give several Metalex or **condition*** treatments to help recondition hair. Use permanent wave lotions especially prepared for lightened and tinted hair. Dilute them further in water. Wind the hair with water and apply the lotion after the hair has been wound. Make frequent tests. An application of **condition*** to the hair before the wave is given will give it more body and help to wave it more successfully.

Porosity—Difficulties Encountered

58. TROUBLESOME POROSITY—HOW TO RECOGNIZE IT

PROBLEM: Improper color development.

CAUSE: Hair has been over-lightened, over-permanented, over-tinted, exposed to sun, salt or over-exposed to other treatments such as hair straighteners. This fragile structure is usually at the end of the hair strand.

SOLUTION: Many problems can be avoided if the operator is able to recognize troublesome porosity and take the necessary precautions or give necessary preliminary treatments before a tint or a permanent wave is attempted.

You should recognize that there are two degrees of porosity:

1. **Desirable** porosity to permit the tint or toner to penetrate satisfactorily. Sometimes the porosity begins to go slightly beyond the desirable amount. This is noted by the color going a little too dark. It is remedied by addition of shampoo to the tint before applying to these areas.

2. **Troublesome** porosity—the "distress area" where hair has been extremely damaged.

    a. *In the early stages of troublesome porosity* the shade finishes too drab, off-color or incomplete looking. Or, ends do not hold sufficient color, color is too weak or too light.

    b. *In the extreme stages of troublesome porosity* hair has been so damaged it holds very little color or does not hold color at all.

HOW TO RECOGNIZE TROUBLESOME POROSITY

Generally, hair that is over-porous feels dry to the touch, breaks easily, when wet stretches easily when pulled on and does not have the snap or bounce unabused hair has. Another observation to make—hair that absorbs moisture very easily is frequently over-porous. The only true way to check porosity and determine to what degree it is over-porous is to give a color Strand Test.

SOLUTION: Use the Clair-Fill shade (chosen from the chart) in the method recommended in Chapter 18 which applies to the problem.

59. INSUFFICIENT POROSITY—HOW TO RECOGNIZE IT

PROBLEM: There is no color-take or poor coverage.

CAUSE: Hair is too resistant.

SOLUTION: In tinting for coverage of gray it may be necessary to pre-soften hair to render hair more porous. In Silver Blonding longer lightening periods are necessary.

Product Performance Other than Normal
60. MISS CLAIROL FOAMS AFTER STANDING

PROBLEM: Sometimes when using Miss Clairol, it will start to foam after it has been mixed and stands for a short while.

CAUSE: This may be caused by shaking or by the fact that the developer or tint has been kept in a warm place such as an overheated room or in sunlight or near a radiator.

SOLUTION: If the tint is mixed in a dish, pour it into a larger dish. If the plastic applicator is used, run cold water over the applicator.

61. TINT OR LIGHTENER TOO THICK

PROBLEM: Tint or lightener may have a very thick consistency when poured. Lightener may become opaque.

CAUSE: 1. Tint or lightener may have been stored at low temperature and frozen. This does not damage the material. 2. Old merchandise. Tint or lightener will take longer to develop.

SOLUTION: If the tint or lightener has been frozen, warm to room temperature before using. If it is old, check your application carefully to allow sufficient development time. (Additional time is needed.) It is important always to check the dates on tint bottles and keep fresh stock on hand.

62. SLOW COLOR OR LIGHTENER DEVELOPMENT— LOW TEMPERATURE

PROBLEM: On cold mornings tint or lightener may take longer than usual to develop.

CAUSE: Cold retards action. Heat speeds action.

SOLUTION: When storing overnight, be sure that the tint you wish to use in the morning is kept away from extreme cold.

63. LIGHTENER MIXTURE TOO FROTHY

PROBLEM: When using lighteners which require beating, you may find the material becoming too frothy and light, making it difficult to pack.

CAUSE: Mixture has been exposed to metal either by use of a metal dish or inferior beater.

SOLUTION: For best results, use a plastic or glass dish and a good stainless steel beater. Beaters with thin stainless steel coatings are not advisable because the stainless steel wears off rapidly.

64. TINT OR LIGHTENER MIXTURE TOO FROTHY—IMPURE DEVELOPER

PROBLEM: Sometimes when tint or lightener is mixed with developer, it immediately begins to froth and double and triple itself in quantity.

CAUSE: Impure developer.

SOLUTION: Discard the mixture and prepare a new mixture using another bottle of developer. Not all developers are chemically pure. When using Clairol products, best results can be obtained by using Clairoxide on Pure White Creme Developer which are laboratory tested to produce the best results.

65. USED TINT

PROBLEM: Saving unused portions of tint for future use.

CAUSE: This is an economical thing to do. It becomes especially important when more than one shade is being used for a treatment and you find yourself with two or more half-used bottles of tint.

SOLUTION: Some light colors are still good for a treatment a week later and very light colors for a day or two. Dark shades are kept longer than that. When two colors are mixed on one patron, you may combine the unused portions in one bottle. This leaves no room for air space; therefore, the tint is preserved for many months. You can then reuse this mixture on the same patron. Be sure to mark combinations on the bottle.

NOTE: Tints or lighteners *must not* be saved after mixing with developer.

Red Colors

66. RED COLORS—GRAY HAIR TURNS ORANGE

PROBLEM: When using a red color which has given satisfactory results in the past, it is sometimes found that too much orange develops at the temples or front hairline.

CAUSE: This usually happens when the patron has become considerably grayer since the treatments were first started. The red colors on the new gray hair do not go as deep as on the rest of the head and consequently turn orange. This is because of the lack of basic pigment in gray hair.

SOLUTION: This may be corrected in one of the following ways:

1. Apply the regular color throughout the hair except at the white areas. At these areas apply one shade deeper.

2. Apply the regular color throughout the hair except at the white portion. At this area add to the balance 3 or 4 capfuls of an Ash Blonde shade. (For instance, in Miss Clairol the color would be Moongold. In Salon Formula it would be Ash Blonde 15E.) This artificially replaces the missing pigment, and the color will be uniform throughout the head.

NOTE: If this orange tone is discovered after a treatment is finished, it can be overcome by applying to the orange area only a mixture of 3 capfuls of Ermine with 3 capfuls of developer. Test for color immediately. If the hair has not drabbed and deepened enough, allow the color to develop for a few minutes and retest. This should only take minutes. Do not overdevelop or too much red will be drabbed.

67. RED COLORS—NOT ENOUGH RED

PROBLEM: Sometimes even though the brightest red color is used, hair does not take on enough red tone to satisfy the patron.

CAUSE: This can be caused by the quality and condition of the hair, most frequently by over-porosity.

SOLUTION: Use one of the three Clair-Fill shades: Brilliant Gold, Pink-Red or Red (whichever fills the color need). If the over-porous condition is extreme, apply Clair-Fill before application of the tint. If only a slight adjustment in color is needed, apply Clair-Fill as soap cap as part of the coloring treatment.

68. RED COLORS—ENDS DO NOT HOLD COLOR

PROBLEM: When tinting with the bright red colors, the ends do not hold color.

CAUSE: This is caused by the ends becoming over-porous. This could be due to permanent waving, over-lightening, sun-bleaching, etc.

SOLUTION: This may be corrected with either of the following methods:

1. These bright colors are generally produced with Red Fashion Colors. When this problem occurs, mix only one-half of the quantity. Apply to the roots in the usual way, using one part color, one part Lady Clairol and two parts developer. But when blending through to the ends, do not carry the original mixture through. Make a new mixture using one part color and one part developer and apply to ends. Using a more concentrated color on the ends will give an even shade throughout.

2. Make the correction using the filler, Clair-Fill, either in Pink-Red or Red. If the ends are slightly faded, apply during the retouch treatment. If ends are not holding color at all, apply Clair-Fill before the retouch to the faded ends.

69. RED COLORS—TO BRIGHTEN RED HIGHLIGHTS ON TINTED HAIR

PROBLEM: Patron would like to brighten her hair which is already tinted to a red shade.

CAUSE: Sometimes a slight brown quality is developed by over-porosity due to over-exposure to sun, over-permanenting, too much lacquer, improper lightening, etc.

SOLUTION: Apply one of the three Clair-Fill shades: Brilliant-Gold, Pink-Red or Red (whichever highlight is required to make the correction). If problem is not serious, apply the filler during the retouch treatment. If decided change to the redder cast is desired, apply the filler before application of tint.

70. RED COLORS—PURPLE OR MAHOGANY TONES

PROBLEM: Hair tinted with red colors takes on objectionable mahogany or purple tones.

CAUSE: This may be caused by the reaction of the particular patron's hair to the color used.

SOLUTION: This may be corrected with either of the following methods:

1. Add a small amount of gold to the color used. For example: If a red color of Miss Clairol is used, use $\frac{1}{4}$ Golden Apricot with $\frac{3}{4}$ of the selected color. If Salon Formula is used, use $\frac{1}{4}$ of either 10A or 11A with $\frac{3}{4}$ of the Salon Formula color.

2. Or add to soap cap the filler, Clair-Fill, in one of three shades: Gold, Golden Brilliant or Red to provide the desired gold.

Removing Tint
71. TINT REMOVING—INADEQUATE APPLICATION

PROBLEM: Uneven results after a tint removing or treatment.

CAUSE: Inadequate application of tint remover. Sometimes the hair is not sufficiently saturated. This condition can also be caused by the fact that the hair is not covered well enough, and the heating cap resting against this portion dries the mixture and stops its action.

SOLUTION: A new mixture must be made and applied to the uneven section in sufficient quantity. Of course, this does not apply to the portion of the hair which is new growth. Virgin hair is not affected by tint removers. Only the tinted portion will change color.

72. TINT REMOVER—FINAL RESULTS UNEVEN

PROBLEM: After final tint remover treatments have been given, and hair is ready to be tinted, a uniform light streak appears throughout the hair. An even shade will be desired.

CAUSE: This streak indicates that the hair at one time had been treated with a lightener that lightened its base. The tint which is now being removed had been applied over the lightener. Therefore, when the tint remover went to work, it exposed the lightened area.

SOLUTION: Here are two ways in which the desired even shade may be achieved:

1. If the coloring to be used is darker than the darkest portion, apply the tint in the usual manner. The light portions will take color more readily, and the color will even itself out.

2. If the color used is lighter than the darkest portion, first lighten the dark portion to a shade as light as the remainder. Then proceed with the coloring desired or use a Miss Clairol color with sufficient lightening action and apply it to the dark spots first.

73. OBJECTIONABLE ODOR AFTER TINT REMOVER TREATMENT

PROBLEM: Often patrons object to odor left in hair after tint remover treatment.

CAUSE: The chemicals in the preparation cause this.

SOLUTION: This can be modified after the final rinse by rinsing with a mixture of 3 to 5 drops of essence of oil of peppermint in one pint of warm water or 3 to 5 drops of essence of lavender in one pint of warm water. No after-rinse should be given.

74. LIGHTENING FOLLOWING TINT REMOVER TREATMENT (AFTER 24 HOURS)

PROBLEM: Lightener is applied the required 24 hours after the tint remover treatment. In spite of this, hair goes very dark or black.

CAUSE: This may be caused by one of two things:

1. Insufficient rinsing of tint remover after treatment.

2. Insufficient number of tint remover treatments given.

In both cases color remains in the hair and resets itself when lightener is applied.

SOLUTION: Rinse lightener from the hair immediately. Reapply dye remover in the regular manner. Wait from 24 to 48 hours. Then give a single color Strand Test to predetermine the results. If the color again is dark, the dye remover treatments must be continued. This could have been avoided in the first place if single Strand Tests were given instead of applying lightener to the whole head at once.

75. TINTING AFTER TINT REMOVER TREATMENT— RESISTANCE TO COLOR

PROBLEM: In tinting 24 hours after a tint remover treatment, the hair becomes extremely difficult to color.

CAUSE: Some textures of hair become harsh after a tint remover treatment, and color does not penetrate the shaft easily.

SOLUTION: Lighten the hair with Ultra-Blue without Protinator (30 minutes), with Neutral Clairolite (30 to 40 minutes) or either Lady Clairol (Instant Whip or Whipped Creme) without the Booster (15 to 20 minutes). Shampoo or rinse very thoroughly. Take a color **Strand** Test. If satisfactory, proceed with entire treatment.

76. TINT DIRECTLY AFTER TINT REMOVER TREATMENT

PROBLEM: Although it is inadvisable to apply a tint over a tint remover without a lapse of 24 hours, an emergency may arise in which the patron demands a tint immediately after the treatment.

CAUSE: The chemicals involved may darken the hair within several hours to as deep a shade as the patron had before the decoloring began.

SOLUTION: It is important not to promise your patron good results and to impress upon her that this is done at her own risk. After the tint remover has been applied in the regular manner and the hair has been shampooed, rinse thoroughly in tepid water for about 5 minutes. Time yourself to be sure that you allow this much time. Towel dry and take a Strand Test for color using a color several shades lighter than the patron desires. If the test is satisfactory, apply the tint in the usual manner, testing frequently. Use no pomades, creams, lacquers for 24 hours after the color treatment.

WARNING: Remember that no matter how perfect the results immediately after tinting there is a possibility that the color will go dark during the next 24 hours.

Roots
77. ROOTS TOO DARK

PROBLEM: Roots darker than balance of hair shaft.

CAUSE: Over-development of color. This may be due to any of the following reasons:

1. A slow application.

2. Mixture left on too long.

3. Too dark a color selected.

4. Peroxide used which is stronger than the required 20-volume

SOLUTION: Remove the excess tint by lightening the over-developed section with one of the following:

1. Lady Clairol Whipped Creme Hair Lightener or Instant Whip Lady Clairol.

2. Neutral Clairolite.

3. Ultra-Blue Lady Clairol.

4. Miss Clairol—⅔ oz. Topaz or Flaxen Blonde, ⅓ oz. Ermine—for cases where the roots are just a shade or two too dark.

5. On very dark and difficult cases where decoloring is necessary, the Booster should be used with either Lady Clairol (Instant Whip or Whipped Creme). Or use Protinator with Ultra-Blue.

In all these cases the application should be watched very closely and the lightening agent should be rinsed as soon as enough coloring has been removed. If this is done, a reapplication of tint can be avoided. If during the lightening the hair goes lighter or redder than desired, reapply a tint to get the desired shade.

78. LIGHT ROOTS WITH MISS CLAIROL ON PREVIOUSLY TINTED HAIR

PROBLEM: When dark Miss Clairol colors are used on a retouch over hair previously tinted with a shampoo tint, the roots may look lighter and warmer than the rest of the hair.

CAUSE: Miss Clairol has lightening action. When applied to hair darker than the color used, it will lighten it a shade or two rather than deepen it as a shampoo tint will do.

SOLUTION: Reapply the same color of Miss Clairol, but add to it a small quantity of Black Velvet (from 1 capful to ⅛ oz., depending on how much depth is needed) or mix with the next deepest color. You may also use a deeper color.

Tint Backs and Changing Color of Tinted Hair

79. RETURNING OVER-POROUS TINTED HAIR TO NATURAL COLOR

PROBLEM: Shade runs too drab. Patron wishes lively color of natural hair.

CAUSE: Improper lightening has left hair over-porous.

SOLUTION: Select shade of Clair-Fill needed to avoid the problem and provide needed deep, warm base. Apply before or during the tinting treatment.

80. RETURNING TINTED HAIR TO NATURAL COLOR

PROBLEM: Patron who has hair lightened and tinted wishes to return to her natural shade.

CAUSE: There can be many reasons for this.

SOLUTION: If there is only a few weeks' growth (½ inch or less), use the Miss Clairol color which is closest to the exact shade desired or a Salon Formula color one shade lighter. Apply to ¾ of the strand, leaving the ends till last. Then start testing for color. As soon as the hair is almost colored enough, carry the balance of the tint through to the ends. If a light color is used, do not dilute with shampoo for the ends. If a dark color is used, add an equal amount of shampoo before working it through the ends.

81. CHANGING TINTED HAIR TO A MUCH LIGHTER SHADE

PROBLEM: Patron wishes to change her hair to a much lighter shade than she now has.

CAUSE: Woman with gray hair realizes lighter colors are much more becoming to her.

SOLUTION: The best solution for this problem is to give patron a Remov-zit application and 24 hours later continue treatment. However, if patron does not have sufficient time for Remov-zit treatment, then do 'the complete treatment with lightening and avoid a waiting period. Lighten hair with either Lady Clairol—or, if hair is resistant, with either Lady Clairol and Lightening Booster, Ultra-Blue and 2 or 3 (if hair is strong, resistant and in good condition) Protinator Envelopes, or in extreme cases with Blue Lightening Powder Bleach. Then tint hair with desired color.

82. CHANGING TINTED HAIR TO LIGHTER SHADE

PROBLEM: The patron has been tinting her hair to one of the dark shades and wishes to lighten her color to a new shade.

CAUSE: There can be many reasons for this, but it is usually due to the fact that a woman who is turning gray realizes that her appearance will improve with a lighter shade.

SOLUTION: First lighten the hair to the shade desired with one of the following: Neutral Oil Bleach, Miss Clairol Topaz with double Clairoxide, Whipped Creme, Instant Whip or Ultra-Blue Lady Clairol. Apply the mixture only to the tinted portion. Then rinse, dry and proceed with the retouch using the desired shade.

83. TINT BACK TO NATURAL A HEAD OF HAIR THAT HAS BEEN PREVIOUSLY TIPPED THROUGHOUT

PROBLEM: To give an even shade throughout.

CAUSE: The lightened hair tips are generally so highly lightened throughout that this hair takes color differently. Sometimes the shade goes drabber on these areas, sometimes darker.

SOLUTION: Apply a warm Clair-Fill shade throughout, choosing the shade that is closest to desired result. There will be no color change in the pigmented hair. Apply throughout for 20 minutes, rinse and towel dry. Proceed with tint.

84. CHANGING COLOR OVER SILVER BLONDE

PROBLEM: Patron with Silver Blonde hair wishes to change her hair from the silver shade to another. Difficulty is encountered.

CAUSE: This is difficult because over-lightened hair will not hold color. All shades including the golds and reds have a tendency to turn drab.

SOLUTION: For best results, one of the following procedures should be used depending upon the color desired.

1. Brown or Black—If Miss Clairol is used, select the exact color desired. If Salon Formula is used, select a color two shades lighter. Apply to the roots first. Then immediately comb through ¾ of the strand. Test frequently for color. When the color is almost as deep as desired, add shampoo to the remainder of the hair and work through the entire head. Allow to develop until desired color is reached. *In cases where color won't hold, apply Clair-Fill first.*

2. Golden Blonde—In Silver Blonding, all gold tones are usually destroyed. It is therefore necessary to artificially replace some of this color.

This is done in one of the following ways:

a. Apply Clair-Fill Pale Gold, Gold or Brilliant Gold before tint application or add it to the tint and apply during retouch treatment.

b. Apply Buttercup Beige mixed with equal developer in same manner as regular tint. Allow to develop from 20 to 40 minutes until test strand shows hair is holding gold tones. In extreme cases a second application may be needed.

c. Shampoo and towel dry the hair. Apply Strawberry Blonde Salon Formula without developer to the entire strand excluding that portion 1 inch from the scalp (this is because some gold tones usually remain in this portion). Distribute the color evenly by combing. Do not rinse. (Since no developer is used, the color would rinse out completely.) Select a color from the gold or warm series. Apply in the usual manner, directly over the Strawberry Blonde.

d. Or use Miss Clairol Sun Bronze with two parts developer. Apply in the same manner. If, however, the hair appears to take too much color, rinse the hair before applying the tint.

3. Red Colors—Apply the tint first to the ends. This is necessary because when working on silvered hair with red colors, the big problem is to get enough color in the ends. When the ends begin to hold color, work the balance of the tint through the entire head like a soap cap. Keep testing. When the shade appears even, rinse and shampoo.

If the ends appear to lose color during a retouch, it is advisable to carry the tint through without diluting until the ends hold enough color.

In very troublesome cases apply Clair-Fill (Brilliant Gold, Pink-Red or Red) before tint application or add to Red Fashion Color and apply during color treatment.

Tint Results Unsatisfactory
85. UNSATISFACTORY TINT RESULTS—SYSTEMIC CAUSES

PROBLEM: Occasionally unsatisfactory results will occur in a tint or lightening treatment even though the application is perfect and the merchandise is in good condition.

CAUSE: Patron's systemic condition may differ from time to time. Poor health may affect the action of lightener or tint. Drugs or anesthetics taken before the treatment may also have an affect.

SOLUTION: Give several reconditioning treatments with Metalex or **condition*** to improve the quality of the hair.

86. DARK ENDS

PROBLEM: Dark ends result after a Miss Clairol treatment or Shampoo Tint.

CAUSE: Insufficient dilution of tint when carried through the ends. The more porous the ends, the darker the results.

SOLUTION: This can be corrected by applying a lightener to the ends. It can also be corrected by using a mixture of 1 oz. Topaz, ½ oz. Ermine and 3 oz. Clairoxide or 1 oz. Flaxen Blonde and 3 oz. Clairoxide. For further treatments apply **condition*** first to the ends and remember to dilute the tint with a greater amount of shampoo, and do not leave it on ends too long.

87. COLOR TOO WEAK

PROBLEM: After color application, the shade may appear too light.

CAUSE: Improper color selection.

SOLUTION: Select a deeper color. First, Strand Test. If, however, this color is too dark, mix the originally selected color with a proportionate amount of the next deeper color or with a few capfuls of Miss Clairol Black Velvet.

88. COLOR TOO DRAB

PROBLEM: After a color treatment the shade appears a bit too drab.

CAUSE: Improper color selection or over-porous condition of hair.

SOLUTION: Warm tones and highlights can be added immediately by applying a Clair-Fill shade with enough warmth in it to add desired warm tones.

221

89. DRABBING OUT RED AND GOLD TONES

PROBLEM: Too many red and gold tones remain after tinting.

CAUSE: This can either be due to an overabundance of red pigment in the hair or improper color selection.

SOLUTION: Give a soap cap using a mixture of 1 oz. Miss Clairol Ermine, 1 oz. Clairoxide and 1 oz. Clairol Shampoo. Work into a lather and test every 5 minutes. When color has drabbed enough, rinse and shampoo. For greater drabbing use a mixture of 1 oz. Miss Clairol Starlight, 1 oz. Clairoxide and 1 oz. Clairol Shampoo.

90. UNEVEN TONING—GOLD STREAKS

PROBLEM: In a Silver Blonde treatment sometimes the resulting shade is gold rather than silver.

CAUSE: Insufficient lightening. Unless the hair is made light enough and porous enough, it will not absorb a sufficient amount of the silver toner even during a long development period. This may occur in spots or in streaks rather than throughout the entire head.

SOLUTION: Prepare another lightening mixture and apply only to the gold spots for additional lightening in this area. The color will not be evenly drab until the base has been evened by lightening. Or apply Clair-Fill #7 Platinum to these gold spots or streaks to help this problem.

91. RED TONES IN BLACK COLORS

PROBLEM: A reddish tone may develop while tinting in the black or blue colors.

CAUSE: This may be due to one of the following reasons:

1. Developer too weak.
2. Insufficient development time.
3. Application not heavy enough.
4. Insufficient penetration because of coated hair.
5. Use of a strong shampoo or rinse which strips color.

SOLUTION: Apply the tint as heavily as possible. If necessary, reapply a second time. Allow the tint to develop from 5 to 10 minutes longer than during previous treatments. Suggest that your patron use Clairol, the colorfast shampoo, Green for Tint and lasting rinse users, and avoid creme rinses that may tend to strip color. Using Pure White Creme Developer instead of a liquid peroxide may produce a drabber result.

92. UNSATISFACTORY COLOR—TOO DARK

PROBLEM: Haircoloring has a tendency to go too dark.

CAUSE: Hair too porous from improper lightening, tinting or permanent waving.

SOLUTION: Use either of the following methods:

1. Recondition with two or three Metalex treatments or a **condition*** treatment. Then select a lighter color or weaken the previously selected color by adding a little of the next lighter color to produce a lighter result.

2. Apply **condition*** to the shaft first; then bring the tint down over the **condition***.

93. VERY DARK OR BLACK ENDS

PROBLEM: While tinting with darker colors, ends become too dark or even black. This must be corrected immediately.

CAUSE: This may be caused either by the fact that the ends are too porous or by insufficient dilution of tint for the ends.

SOLUTION: 1. Make a highly diluted solution of Remov-zit. Apply to only the dark ends or sections. It is advisable to do this at the basin. Test for color as soon as application is complete, and continue to test frequently. It is important to time this correctly so that the Remov-zit can be rinsed out when the hair has reached the right shade. If the mixture is left on too long, the hair will go red and too light. In this case, additional color will have to be added. This cannot be done for 24 hours.

2. Lighten with Ultra-Blue with 1, 2 or 3 Protinator Envelopes. To avoid the problem in the future use **condition*** first on the ends; then bring tint down over it.

94. FADED OR STREAKED ENDS—VIRGIN BLONDE OR RED HAIR

PROBLEM: Patron has virgin blonde or red hair streaked or faded at the ends. She may want the condition to be corrected, but not want to have her hair colored regularly.

CAUSE: This condition may be caused by sun-streaking or by a permanent wave.

SOLUTION: This may be corrected as follows:

1. The best way is with Loving Care, matching the hair with the appropriate Loving Care shade.

2. Apply to the light area only the Miss Clairol color closest to the patron's natural shade. It is mixed in the regular way with an equal amount of Clairoxide. If Salon Formula is used, select the color closest to the natural shade and mix it with equal parts of developer and shampoo. A few minutes after application, start testing for color. As soon as color is even, rinse immediately and shampoo.

95. TOO MUCH RED IN DRABBEST SHADES

PROBLEM: On some customers even the drabbest shades have a tendency to turn red after a period of time.

CAUSE: This may be caused by any of the following reasons:

1. Unsatisfactory tint treatment because of weak developer.

2. Bad application of tint or insufficient quantity used.

3. Fading from underdevelopment of color.

4. Stripping of color due to the use of improper shampoos or excessive use of lacquers and pomades.

5. Too much natural red pigment in the hair.

SOLUTION: If checkup shows that reason 1, 2 or 3 applies, reapply the tint and allow to develop further.

If reason 4 or 5 applies, correction can be made in one of the following ways:

1. Add 1/4 Miss Clairol Ermine to 3/4 of the color selected.

2. If a Strand Test shows that the Ermine does not produce a drab enough color, the same quantity of Miss Clairol Starlight should be substituted.

3. Add Clairol Silver Drops. If Salon Formula colors are used, add 3 or 4 drops. If Miss Clairol colors are used, add 5 to 10 drops.

4. To avoid the problem in the future shampoo with Clairol, the color-fast shampoo, Green for Tint and lasting rinse users.

96. FADED OR STREAKED ENDS—VIRGIN BROWN HAIR

PROBLEM: Patron has virgin brown hair streaked or faded at the ends. She may want the condition to be corrected but not want to have her hair colored regularly.

CAUSE: This condition may be caused by sun-streaking or by a permanent wave.

SOLUTION: The preferred method is to use Loving Care in a shade to match the hair. Or this may be corrected by applying color to the light areas. With brown hair the color to be used might be Sable Brown or Black Velvet (Miss Clairol) without developer, or Salon Formula 18, 19 or 20 without developer. A few minutes after application, start testing for color. When color is even, rinse immediately and shampoo.

97. LOVING CARE DRAB SHADE FINISHES TOO WARM

PROBLEM: After treatment with drab shade, result is still too warm.

CAUSE: Hair has a natural tendency for warm highlights.

SOLUTION: Add 2 to 6 capfuls of Silk & Silver. For slight drabbing use #11, for moderate drabbing #13, and for deep drabbing #15. Strand Test first to determine best mixture to make.

98. LOVING CARE—INSUFFICIENT COLOR-TAKE

PROBLEM: Upon finishing the Loving Care treatment, the coverage is incomplete.

CAUSE: Hair is resistant due to the structure and texture.

SOLUTION: Allow the Loving Care shade to develop for 30 minutes. With a towel wipe off as much as possible and reapply a fresh mixture of the same shade. Put plastic cap back on patron again. Develop for another 20 minutes or more if Strand Test indicates it is necessary.

99. LOVING CARE COVERAGE INSUFFICIENT

PROBLEM: Loving Care coverage insufficient.

CAUSE: Hair is extremely resistant, making it difficult to color.

SOLUTION: After rinsing, reapply the same shade of Loving Care immediately, and *be sure* to work the mixture into the hair with the fingers to as complete a lather as possible.

100. LOVING CARE SHADES NEED LIGHTENING

PROBLEM: Loving Care shade too dark.

CAUSE: Wrong color selection.

SOLUTION: Make a mixture of 1 oz. Metalex and 1 oz. Clairoxide or Pure White Creme Developer. Apply to hair, saturating thoroughly with the mixture. Leave hair uncovered 20 to 30 minutes. For best results this mixture should be applied immediately after rinsing Loving Care from the hair. Do not dry hair under a dryer as this sets color and makes it more difficult to lighten.

101. CUSTOMER'S REQUEST—COVER ONLY GRAY AND LEAVE NATURAL HAIR ALONE

PROBLEM: Retaining natural color while covering or blending gray.

CAUSE: In the past this has been next to impossible because of change hair went through while tinting. Always there was a lightening, deepening or reddening of the natural hair to some degree.

SOLUTION: A Loving Care treatment closest to the natural shade of the patron's hair.

102. SILK & SILVER—TOO BLUE OR MAUVE

PROBLEM: After a Silk & Silver treatment, hair is too blue or mauve.

CAUSE: Due to structure or peculiarity of the hair it has a tendency to go into the blue tones.

SOLUTION: To correct a treatment that went too blue, work throughout the hair quickly for a minute or two Loving Care #73 Ash Blonde. If the Preliminary Strand Test shows #73 lifted too much of the color, mix #73 Loving Care with an equal amount of water before applying to the head.

To avoid the problem in the future, add 1, 2 or 3 capfuls of #73 Ash Blonde Loving Care to the Silk & Silver shade or dilute with #10 Silk & Silver. Strand Test to determine the best proportion.

103. SILK & SILVER—SHADE JUST APPLIED A LITTLE TOO DEEP

PROBLEM: After Silk & Silver treatment is finished, shade is a little darker than desired results.

CAUSE: Wrong color selection.

SOLUTION: Apply Metalex throughout the hair, saturating it thoroughly, immediately after treatment is given. Do not dry hair under the dryer, since this makes it more difficult to lighten the hair.

104. SILK & SILVER—SHADE A LITTLE TOO DARK, PATRON RETURNS, WISHES IT LIGHTER

PROBLEM: After patron has worn shade she wishes it lightened since she feels it is a little too dark.

CAUSE: Wrong color selection.

SOLUTION: Mix 1 oz. Metalex, 1 oz. Clairoxide or Pure White Creme Developer and saturate hair with solution. Leave on hair 20 to 30 minutes. Do not cover hair with plastic cap.

105. LOVING CARE SHADE TOO DRAB

PROBLEM: Shade too drab.

CAUSE: Wrong color selection.

SOLUTION: Add 1 to 3 capfuls of #74 (Reddish Blonde) or 1 or 2 capfuls of #80 (Auburn) to the Loving Care shade you are using when giving the next treatment.

106. TOO MUCH COLOR AT ROOTS AFTER SPARKLING COLOR TREATMENT

PROBLEM: After application of Sparkling Color on a light head, the blonde or red shades result in too intense a shade at the roots and weaker on the shaft and ends.

CAUSE: This is due to variation of hair texture, the hair at the root being one texture and the hair at shaft being another. Sometimes it may be due to dryness, brittleness, coatings, permanent waves, etc.

CORRECTION: Apply Sparkling Color Light Brown to the root area only. Let it set for a few minutes, then start testing. As soon as the color at the root area is subdued enough, rinse the brown from the hair.

(Do not bring the brown down through the shaft.) In the future to avoid this condition use one of the following two procedures:

1. Apply Sparkling Color to the hair shaft first, omitting the roots until later.

2. Mix a part of the Sparkling Color to be used with a small amount of Light Brown. Confine this to the root area only, then apply to the shaft, omitting the light brown mixture.

107. DISCOLORATION—AFTER SPARKLING COLOR TREATMENT

PROBLEM: After a treatment with the brown shades of Sparkling Color (particularly the dark ones), color has a tendency to go purple (mahogany) on strands, ends or throughout.

CAUSE: Hair has been lightened or bleached by sun, permanent waves, etc.

CORRECTION: The haircolorist must be reminded to keep Sparkling Color off bleached hair to avoid this problem in the future.

To improve the color so that the discoloration is not as obvious (and in some cases to correct the problem completely) do the following:

Apply #75 Loving Care to discolored areas, allow it to develop for a few minutes and start testing immediately. Continue testing until the discoloration is covered sufficiently and the shades appear to blend in with the color throughout. When this stage is reached, stop the action by rinsing thoroughly and be sure to give the Loving Care After-Rinse in the usual manner.

NOTE: If #75 results a little on the dark side, either mix it with #73 or switch to #73 for the correction. If #75 is not taking enough, add #77 to it and in the future you may resort to #77 alone. Be sure to stay in the drab family, omitting the use of #79 unless you have pre-tested first. Although Loving Care can be used as a corrective treatment *do not mix* Loving Care and Sparkling Color together for future treatments . . . these are not compatible.

108. SPARKLING COLOR RUBS OFF

PROBLEM: Infrequently there is a rub-off of Sparkling Color on combs and brushes.

CAUSE: In any instance the application is at fault since the rub-off is only due to the following:

1. Applying Sparkling Color to hair that has not been thoroughly cleansed before the application.

2. At the end of the color development, the Sparkling Color was not worked into a full enough lather.

3. There has not been sufficient rinsing at the end to remove the excess residue.

4. An after-rinse of some kind has been used that will remove any color.

CORRECTION: Take precautions in the future to correct above conditions.

Shampooing

109. HARD WATER—INSUFFICIENT LATHER

PROBLEM: In hard water regions it is difficult for some shampoos to cleanse the hair properly.

CAUSE: Chemicals prevalent in hard water.

SOLUTION: 1. Add Sylk to shampoo. This will greatly increase the amount of lather. It will also allow you to use less shampoo.

2. Use new Clairol, the colorfast shampoo, Green for Tint and lasting rinse users, or Clairol, the colorfast shampoo, Blue for Lightened and Toned Hair. Both concentrates lather well in hard water.

110. RELIEVING SNARLS AND TANGLES ON TINTED AND LIGHTENED HAIR

PROBLEM: Products may be used to remove snarls and tangles from newly shampooed hair. On tinted hair, however, many of these products have a tendency to remove the color.

CAUSE: Decoloring is caused by the chemical reaction of these products on the haircoloring. This is particularly true of creme rinses.

SOLUTION: This may be avoided through the use of Clairol Hair-So-New. Hair-So-New is applied to the hair immediately after the shampoo or a newly given tint. It removes the snarls and tangles instantly but has no effect upon color.

111. COLOR UNEVEN FROM COLORED SHAMPOOS

PROBLEM: Hair takes color unevenly.

CAUSE: On the same head of hair there are different degrees of porosity. Since colored shampoos are shampooed into the hair—not applied like tints—it is difficult to secure an even color throughout.

SOLUTION: Apply Metalex to just those areas that have taken too much color. Test after a few minutes, and as soon as color is lifted, rinse. If the color shampoo is of a more lasting type, it may have to be removed by lightening, if hair has been previously exposed to lightener. If the color shampoo has been used on natural hair, in extreme cases highly diluted Remov-zit should be used.

Special Problems

112. LIGHTENING—PATRON IS ALLERGIC TO COLOR

PROBLEM: Tint has been added during lightening to give additional drab effect. Patron develops allergy to tint but wishes to continue to lighten her hair.

CAUSE: Even the smallest amount of penetrating color used in lighteners may be enough to cause sensitivity in an allergic person.

SOLUTION: Substitute either neutral or color lighteners depending upon the amount of drabness desired. When extreme drabbing is desired, use either Clairolite Sparkling Silver or Clairolite Silver (Drab) Oil Bleach or Ultra-Blue Lady Clairol, alone or with 1 or 2 Protinator Envelopes according to the need.

113. IRRITATION OF HANDS FROM LIGHTENERS

PROBLEM: Often after giving several lightening treatments, operators working without gloves find that their fingers become sensitive, and the skin tissues turn white.

CAUSE: Chemicals in lighteners may affect skin. Rubber gloves should be used at all times.

SOLUTION: To relieve discomfort, apply regular household vinegar. This will neutralize the action and stop the discomfort, or wash hands with Loving Care Creme After Rinse.

114. ITCHY SCALP

PROBLEM: Some tint customers develop a very itchy scalp during a color treatment.

CAUSE: It is possible for a person to have such a sensitivity without having a prohibitive allergy.

SOLUTION: First, it is wise to reascertain whether or not an allergy exists by giving another Skin Test. If no reaction develops, you may proceed with the tint. Sometimes the itchiness can be avoided by asking the customer not to shampoo her hair a week or 10 days before the treatment and not to brush the day of the treatment. Be sure that a skin test is given before each treatment. In the Patch Test use the exact shade of tint that is used in the treatment.

115. OVERSENSITIVE SCALP

PROBLEM: Instances may occur where patron has a scalp which is extremely sensitive to lightener or tint without being allergic. This patron may desire to continue the tint treatment regardless of the discomfort.

SOLUTION: Some of the discomfort may be alleviated by mixing either the tint or lightener and letting it stand in an open dish for 5 or 6 minutes before applying to the head. Development time may have to be extended in this case. Using Ultra Blue Lady Clairol instead of the other lightener, may also help.

116. SCALP STAINS IN PATCHES

PROBLEM: Occasionally a customer may have tint stains on the scalp in patches.

CAUSE: A systemic scalp condition.

SOLUTION: Apply some of the same tint used on a piece of cotton and gently rub the stains. As soon as they are lifted, rinse the scalp. Then shampoo.

117. STAINING SCALP WITH TINT

PROBLEM: After a color treatment you may find that brown or black shades are not removed from the scalp.

CAUSE: A dry or scaly scalp may cause this.

SOLUTION: This can be relieved by adding ½ tsp. Sylk to the coloring mixture after the regular development time. Then dilute with shampoo and work it through the entire head. This will help lift the coloring from the scalp without removing color from the hair shaft.

118. STAINING SKIN WITH TINT

PROBLEM: Neck, face or forehead may become stained while tinting.

CAUSE: This may be caused by careless application.

SOLUTION: Wipe off immediately. If color does not come off, add a few drops of the same tint to a towel or piece of cotton and rub the spot gently. Then wipe immediately with a clean cloth. The use of a small amount of Vitapointe will also achieve the same result.

119. LIGHTENER OR TINT IN EYE

PROBLEM: Patron gets some lightener or tint in her eye.

CAUSE: Carelessness. Extreme precaution should be taken to protect the eyes from tint.

SOLUTION: Bathe eye immediately with plenty of water. This stops the action and relieves burning or stinging. Follow with an eye wash.

Streaking

120. CORRECTING DARK STREAKS

PROBLEM: Developer is applied to correct dark streaks in a retouch, but streaked portion goes even darker.

CAUSE: Developer is not rinsed out and continues to develop the color after being heated under the dryer.

SOLUTION: Be careful to rinse out the developer immediately after the streak has lightened.

121. SUN-STREAKED HAIR

PROBLEM: Hair streaked from exposure to sun.

CAUSE: Over-exposure to sun has lightening effect on hair.

SOLUTION: This can be corrected as follows:

1. Apply Loving Care in the shade closest to the patron's natural shade. (This is the preferred method.)
2. Give a shampoo cap with the Miss Clairol color closest to patron's natural color. If there is no single color close enough, mix colors to

achieve proper shade. Color Strand Test should be made frequently. Development seldom exceeds 10 minutes.

122. AVOIDING STREAKED HAIR—COLORED OIL LIGHTENERS

PROBLEM: Patron has over-porous hair, and you wish to avoid streaking during an oil lightening treatment.

CAUSE: Too much color must not be used with porous hair. Excess color will cause the hair to streak.

SOLUTION: First, weaken the coloring value of the lightener by mixing it with the neutral lightener. The amount to be used can be determined by giving a Strand Test. Then apply **condition*** to the hair shaft to help revitalize texture.

123. AVOIDING DARK STREAKS AT TEMPLES

PROBLEM: Some tint patrons always develop dark streaks at the hairline or temples. When this happens, the color must be bleached out, which unfortunately makes the hair more porous and consequently makes it go darker each time. This can be avoided if you know in advance that the condition exists.

CAUSE: This condition usually occurs when the hair is extremely fine and consequently more porous than normal.

SOLUTION: Here are two ways to avoid the condition:

1. As soon as the application to the roots is completed, part the hair ½ inch beyond the hairline and hold the strand perpendicular to the scalp. Use a towel to dry off the tint which has seeped beyond the new growth. This stops the coloring action and is preferable to shampooing because the shampoo may seep to roots and weaken coloring action.

2. Apply **condition*** to these areas first. Then proceed with tinting in usual manner, and when color has developed sufficiently in root area, blend color over areas previously treated with **condition***. Develop until color is even, rinse and shampoo.

124. LIGHT STREAKS ON TINTED OR LIGHTENED HAIR

PROBLEM: Light streaks may develop throughout hair which has been tinted or lightened.

CAUSE: In lightening, light streaks are caused by overlapping, by sun-bleaching, by permanent waving or by tinting.

SOLUTION: Spot tinting will correct the streaks. Select a color deep enough to match darkest portion of hair. Apply only to the light spots. Test frequently. As soon as the light spots have enough color, dilute the balance of the tint with an equal amount of shampoo. (If brown color is used, use twice as much shampoo.) Work into lather to distribute color evenly. Rinse and shampoo.

APPENDIX

THE
STRUCTURE
OF
HAIR

HAIR TINTING is a chemical process. In order to understand the techniques of tinting it is important to know as much as possible about the chemistry and structure of hair.

The Structure of Hair

Hair differs widely in color, thickness, straightness and number. The average head has 100,000 to 150,000 hairs. Blonde heads have up to 140,000 or more. Redheads have about 100,000. The diameter of single hairs varies from 1/140 to 1/1500 of an inch. Even on a single head there are wide variations in the thickness of hair.

HAIR COMPLICATED STRUCTURE

Hair is composed of proteins similar to the other proteins of the body. Its quality and color have been determined before it surfaces the scalp. The hair you see is a perfect barometer of health, vitamin or hormone deficiency, diet and even reflects emotional problems since its growth and function are dependent on all these.

THE GROWING PART OF HAIR

This lies within a tubular indentation of the skin called the follicle. The bottom of the follicle is penetrated by a small upward-growing projection of tissue called the papilla, on which the hair bulb is formed. The part of the hair inside the follicle is the hair root. The part outside is the hair shaft. Popularly, in tinting we speak of "root" as the visible hair adjacent to the scalp.

THE OIL GLANDS

Each hair follicle is supplied with one to six fat-producing oil glands. Their function is to supply an oily wax of butter-like consistency to lubricate the hair, give it lustre and protection. Decreased secretion causes dry hair, while too much fat causes oily hair and skin. Less wax is excreted in cold weather. Children have less oil in their hair than adults. The oily secretion increases sharply in puberty and the last months of pregnancy and on a diet especially rich in carbohydrates and fats. Secretion decreases with advancing age (usually around thirty-five to forty in women and is much slower in men). This slow-up is often the cause of dry scalp and hair in older people.

GROWTH OF HAIR

Hair grows at the rate of 1/3 to 2/5 of an inch each month. Its life span is two to five years; then it falls out. (Normal daily fall out is from 40 to 100 hairs.) As hair falls out, it is replaced through a new column of cells formed in or near the old follicle.

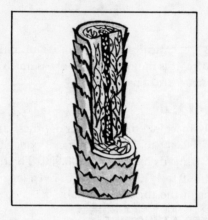

Structure
of the Hair

The Hair Shaft

Haircoloring is applied only to the hair shaft. This is the portion of the hair the colorist is concerned with.

Under the microscope the hair shaft shows three different cell layers. The outer layer is called the *cuticle*. The innermost (much like the lead in a pencil) is called the *medulla*. It's present only intermittently and is often completely absent. The part between the cuticle and the medulla represents the bulk of the hair and is called the *cortex*.

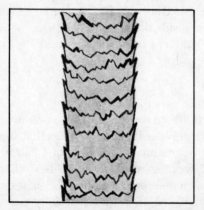

Hair shaft
is covered with
a cuticle layer
of horny, flat cells.

THE CUTICLE

The cuticle of the hair shaft is composed of flat cells which lie on the surface of the hair in overlapping formation, much like fish scales or the shingles on a roof. These cells contain no pigment and are translucent. The toothlike edges of the cuticle are projected upward and are affected by combing and brushing. When hair is combed or brushed away from the scalp, these edges are left smooth; combing or brushing in the opposite direction causes damage.

To allow tint to penetrate to the cortex these scales must be softened.

In tinting, in order for haircoloring to appear natural looking, the coloring must penetrate *inside* the hair shaft to shine through the translucent cuticle layer. (That's what gives good coloring its "lifelike" look.) When the cuticle layer becomes colored—and this happens only when old-fashioned coating types of dyes are used—the haircoloring no longer looks natural.

The cuticle and the membrane are sometimes resistant to penetration of the tint. If this happens, the hair must be pre-softened, pre-lightened or other techniques must be used to make the hair receptive to tints.

THE CORTEX

The cortex layer is composed of cigar-shaped cells, firmly adhering to each other, arranged lengthwise. The natural pigment which gives hair its color is found in this layer. It is here that color changes are made in tinting and lightening.

THE MEDULLA

The medulla is often absent and is unimportant in haircoloring.

What Causes Color in Hair

Hair color is determined in part by hereditary and racial factors. Natural haircoloring is due to the presence of either brown or yellow and red pigments or a mixture of the two.

The combination of these pigments causes the variety of natural hair colors.

These pigments in granular form are called melanin. It is important to understand these pigments because they affect the lightening and tinting processes.

BROWN PIGMENT

The brown pigment is scattered irregularly in granular form, mainly throughout the outer part of the cortex. It is made by the action of an enzyme called tyrosinase from specific amino acids. In lightening, this pigment changes after the application of the lightener. The longer the lightener is left on, the lighter the hair becomes.

YELLOW AND RED PIGMENTS

The yellow and red pigments contain iron. They are present in granular and diffused form in the cortex cells and are harder to destroy by lightening. These yellow and red pigments also cause dark hair to have reddish highlights.

What Causes Gray Hair

The pigments are produced in the hair papilla and deposited in the basal cells which are later converted into the cigar-like cortex cells and are moved upward with the growing hair shaft.

Gray hair is produced by partial or complete absence of the pigment. The remaining pigment granules are irregularly distributed throughout the hair.

New gray or white hair grows from follicles where dark hair has been shed, and in some cases dark hair grows out of the follicles where formerly white or gray hair has been observed.

Ordinarily graying is a gradual process. Starting at the temples, the graying progresses slowly until complete gray or white hair develops.

Prolonged insufficient nutrition affects the growth of hair. There is no proof that feeding of specific vitamins will stop or retard graying under normal conditions.

EYEBROWS AND EYELASHES

The changes in color of the eyebrows and eyelashes are not related to the changes in the color of the hair on the scalp.

CAUTION: Hair tint must not be used on eyelashes or eyebrows.

GLOSSARY OF CLAIROL
HAIRCOLORING AND
HAIR CARE PRODUCTS

Clairol Permanent Haircolorings

THE haircolorist has a whole repertoire of Clairol coloring products in a wide range of shades at her fingertips. They are scientifically formulated by Clairol Research to make her work easy, to pamper the hair and to produce exquisitely beautiful, natural-looking results.

MISS CLAIROL HAIR COLOR BATH—
CREME FORMULA AND REGULAR

The method that has changed the whole concept of haircoloring. Miss Clairol *tints* and *lightens,* conditions and shampoos, too . . . all in one simple operation. Completely covers gray. It gives "haircoloring so natural only her hairdresser knows for sure." There are 13 natural-looking shades and 2 special drabbers that can be mixed with the other Miss Clairol colors.

CLAIROL CREME TONER

The Salon Formula Oil Shampoo Tint that produces unbelievably light, delicate, "high-fashion" blonde shades. There are 32 glamorous colors in all in the 9 Creme Toner color categories: Ash, Silver, Platinum, Neutral, Warm, Beige, the Chiffons, Pearls and Champagnes. To accept these delicate shades hair must always be pre-lightened to gold, yellow or pale yellow (according to the Creme Toner used). Contains rich conditioning oils.

CLAIROL RED FASHION COLORS

Salon Formula Oil Shampoo Tint in the dramatic new red shades. The four Clairol Red Fashion Colors are packaged with Lady Clairol Whipped Creme Hair Lightener. The colors may be used with or without Lady Clairol. A lighter effect is achieved with Lady Clairol.

CLAIROL SALON FORMULA OIL SHAMPOO TINT

It is shampoo and tint in one. Comes in 14 shades for permanent, penetrating haircoloring. Has no lightening action of its own, so hair must be pre-lightened when patron wants shade lighter than her natural one.

Clairol Semi-Permanent Haircolorings

Clairol introduces a new category in haircoloring with three glamorizing new semi-permanent hair color lotions. They contain no peroxide, use no peroxide. But color is self-penetrating, does not rub off, lasts for weeks through shampoo after shampoo. They are:

LOVING CARE HAIR COLOR LOTION

For the woman with graying hair who will not use tints and can't be satisfied with a rinse. It washes away only the gray without changing the hair's original natural color. Color is self-penetrating to give color that lasts for weeks. Not a tint, yet superior to a rinse. There are 11 Loving Care colors to match the patron's natural shade.

SILK & SILVER HAIR COLOR LOTION

Silk & Silver washes shimmering silver into gray or white hair. In 7 entrancing colors to glamorize every gray head of hair. Banishes "problem yellow." Shampoo is built right into the coloring lotion. Conditions hair, too—leaves it silken-soft and manageable.

SPARKLING COLOR HAIR COLOR LOTION

The *only* hair color lotion made for hair untouched by gray. Comes in 7 colors that brighten, highlight and glamorize natural haircolor . . . or add a touch of new color. Contains no peroxide and uses no peroxide. Gently introduces color to the hair and lasts through more than a month of shampoos. Cannot be used on gray or graying hair or on lightened or tinted hair—is a *specific* for natural hair.

Clairol Temporary Haircolorings

Clairol Come Alive Rinses are superior products which give the hair lovely temporary color, silkiness and sparkling highlights. There are 2 Come Alive color groups:

COME ALIVE GRAY

In 4 gray shades for every type of hair from white to pepper-and-salt. Removes yellow discoloration and gives shining, silvery beauty from one shampoo to the next.

COME ALIVE COLORS

Add highlights to natural hair or may be used on graying hair. In Red, Brown and Blonde shades.

Clairol Lighteners

Because the haircolorist encounters so many different problems in lightening hair, Clairol Research offers a whole family of specialized lighteners to meet every need and preference. These are superior products, formulated to protect the hair as well as to remove pigment and make your work easier and faster. Most popular are the three all-purpose Lady Clairol creme lighteners . . . the easiest to apply and most versatile.

These are:

ULTRA-BLUE LADY CLAIROL CREMOGENIZED HAIR LIGHTENER—

This product lightens *lighter* and *more quickly* than any other product on the market. Its creme consistency makes it easy to apply. It gives your patron greater comfort than ever before during lightening. Use Ultra-Blue as an all-purpose lightener and prior to application of high-fashion Clairol Creme Toner shades.

ULTRA-BLUE LADY CLAIROL PROTINATOR

Ultra-Blue Protinator was formulated especially for use with Ultra-Blue Cremogenized Hair Lightener to condition the protein structure of the hair and increase the lightening action of Ultra-Blue Lightener. It can be used *only* with Ultra-Blue.

INSTANT WHIP LADY CLAIROL HAIR LIGHTENER

Instant Whip Lady Clairol becomes creamy instantly when mixed with developer in bowl or applicator. It is used for moderate lightening action. With the addition of Lady Clairol Lightening Booster powder, it may be used for any degree of lightening.

LADY CLAIROL WHIPPED CREME HAIR LIGHTENER

It becomes creamy when mixed with a developer and whipped with an egg beater. Not as fast-acting as the other two Lady Clairol lighteners, it may be used for moderate lightening, or its action speeded and increased by the addition of Lightening Boosters to pre-lighten hair for toning.

LADY CLAIROL LIGHTENING BOOSTER

Is added to Lady Clairol Instant Whip or Lady Clairol Whipped Creme whenever either is used to pre-lighten hair for toning—to increase the speed and lightening action of either. It is never used with Ultra-Blue.

BLUE LIGHTENING

Blue Lightening is an all-purpose lightener in powder form. Has greater speed, lightening and drabbing action than other powdered lighteners. Used when extensive lightening is required on resistant hair and hair is in strong condition. Useful for frosting, tipping and streaking.

CLAIROLITE

Clairolite is a superior mild oil lightener that lightens and brightens hair in one step. Use for slight to moderate lightening. Comes in 4 shades and *Neutral*. The colors add temporary color highlights as they lighten. Neutral has no color, is used to pre-soften hair for tint application.

Clairol Developers

A developer must be mixed with lighteners, tints and toning products to produce final results. The perfect developer is good, fresh, stable 20-volume hydrogen peroxide. Clairol brings it to you in two forms ideal for success in your lightening, tinting and toning work:

PURE WHITE CREME DEVELOPER

The modern creme lotion developer that replaces ordinary peroxide for better hair condition. Proved by the U.S. Testing Company to be the most stable of its kind. Creamy, "stay-put" consistency will not run or drip, making application faster, easier and more comfortable for the patron.

CLAIROXIDE

In liquid form. Helps assure good tinting and lightening results. Both developers remain stable in the unopened bottle.

Clairol Drabbing Agents

Clairol has three drabbing agents to increase the drabbing action of Miss Clairol colors. These are:

MISS CLAIROL ERMINE

Special drabber to be mixed with Miss Clairol colors for extra drabbing.

MISS CLAIROL STARLIGHT

Twice as concentrated as Ermine, for use on hair with a great deal of red pigment where extra drabbing is needed.

SILVER DROPS

Also used to make Miss Clairol colors and all other tints drabber, it is a highly concentrated color that reduces and drabs red or gold tones.

Clairol Conditioning Products

The skillful and successful haircolorist is adept at preventing damage to her patrons' hair and at correcting faulty conditions. These Clairol products are her trusted allies:

condition*

The beauty prescription for troubled hair. **condition*** is a rich creme compounded to revitalize dry, limp, spongy or damaged hair. Used as a general reconditioner or combined with lightening and coloring treatments. Recommended before permanent waves.

METALEX

Metalex restores spring and sheen to hair damaged by over-lightening, over-permanenting or home use of certain hair preparations. Besides reconditioning, Metalex *lifts* metallic-based dyes, rinses, compound hennas and hair restorers that coat the hair and often cause discoloration when a permanent or tint is used.

Color Corrective
CLAIR-FILL
This filler builds color on damaged hair, makes possible even color-take on both over-porous and normal areas for even tone from roots to ends. Comes in 7 shades.

Color Remover
REMOV-ZIT
Removes sufficient penetrating tints or compound hennas for application of fresh color but does not leave the hair pure white or lighten natural pigment.

Clairol Hair Care Products
CLAIROL SHAMPOO - THE COLORFAST FORMULA
Especially formulated to keep the color lovely in color-treated hair. There are two types: (1) Clairol Green for Tint and lasting rinse users and (2) Clairol Blue for Lightened and Toned Hair.

VITAPOINTE CREME HAIRDRESS AND CONDITIONER
The light, white, delicate creme hairdress—never greasy. Adds beautiful sheen and manageability to all kinds of hair. Used after tinting or toning, it will not affect even the most delicate color.

HAIR-SO-NEW
Used like an ordinary setting lotion, it also conditions hair, gives it more body, eliminates snarls. Does not strip color.

SYLK
A water softener.

DICTIONARY OF
HAIRCOLORING
TERMS

After-rinse . . . . A product used, in some cases, after a treatment.

Allergy . . . . A hypersensitivity to certain foods, cosmetics, tints or any other substances due to personal idiosyncrasy. The reaction is not visible on application but usually 6 to 24 hours later.

Aniline . . . . A coal tar derivative used in penetrating tints.

Ash . . . . A shade containing no red or gold tones.

Bleach . . . . A preparation which lightens the hair by removing the pigmentation. The Clairol usage for this term is "lightener."

Bleach Pack . . . . . A bleach solution prepared in a thick consistency.

Blending . . . . . . The process of evening color throughout the hair strand during retouches.

Blonde on Blonde . . . A high-fashion Clairol technique in which two blonde colors are used to achieve a blending of light and dark ash blonde shades.

Blonding . . . . . . The term applied to lightening the hair preparing it for one of the toner shades.

Breakage . . . . . . A condition in which hair splits and breaks off. Caused by over-lightening, improper permanent waving, etc.

Certified Color . . . . A coloring which coats the hair. No Patch Test is necessary when certified colors are used in the product.

Coating . . . . Residue left on the outside of the hair shaft.

Color-builder	A filler to build color on over-porous hair so it can take and hold color evenly.
Color Mixing	Mixing two shades together for an in-between color.
Color Remover	A product designed to remove tint from hair.
Color Test	The process of washing or drying a strand to determine progress during tinting or lightening.
Conditioner	Any product applied to hair to restore oils, sheen, elasticity and manageability.
Coverage	Coloring gray or white hair.
Decolorization	Removal of color from hair.
Developer	Clairoxide, Pure White Creme Developer or a 20-volume peroxide which is mixed with tints and lighteners to produce final results.
Development Time . . .	Time needed to develop the color or the lightener. It begins at completion of application.
Discoloration	When a shade develops off-color, unnatural-looking.
Drab	A shade which contains no red or gold tones. To drab hair means to remove red and gold tones from hair.
Filler	Product or tint used to temporarily provide fill for porous spots in hair during chemical treatments such as permanent waving, lightening.
Frosting	Lightening small sections of hair throughout the head.
Gold Bands	Brassy areas due to insufficient lightening.
Hair Color Lotion . . .	A semi-permanent haircoloring which does not contain or need a developer and which lasts through several shampoos.
Hair Lightener . . .	A product used to decolorize hair to varying degrees.
Hair Shaft	Visible part of each strand of hair. It is made up of an outer layer called the cuticle, an innermost layer called the medulla and an in-between layer called the cortex. The cortex layer is where color changes are made by modern penetrating tints such as Miss Clairol.
Highlighting	Brightening the appearance of hair by adding color tones.

Lightening . . . . . The process of removing pigment from hair, resulting in lightening the hair.

Line of Demarcation . . A streak caused by overlapping on previously tinted hair. Not possible with Miss Clairol.

Metallic Dyes . . . . . Permanent color which contains metal salts.

Over-lap . . . . . . The condition caused when the lightener or tint runs down the hair strand during a retouch.

Over-porosity . . . . . The condition where hair reaches an undesirable stage of porosity requiring correction.

Oxidation . . . . . . The process of development of the tint after Clairoxide or Pure White Creme Developer is added.

Patch Test . . . . . . A skin test given 24 hours prior to a tint treatment to ascertain whether or not a patron is allergic or hypersensitive to the tint. It is required by law for all permanent tints of the oxidizing type.

Penetrating Tint . . . A tint which penetrates into hair shaft and deposits color permanently.

Pepper and Salt . . . . A term used for hair that has a mixture of pigmented and white strands.

Peroxometer . . . . . A device which measures the strength of hydrogen peroxide.

Pigment . . . . . . Coloring matter, either natural or artificial. Red, gold, brown or a combination thereof.

Plastic Applicator . . . Pliable squeeze bottle used for the application of Clairol tints, toners, lighteners and shampoos — eliminating the use of dish, comb, brush or swab. Nozzles are available to suit product consistency.

Plastic Cap . . . . . Cap made of plastic, used in some semi-permanent coloring treatments to help hold in body heat to help color development.

Porosity . . . . The condition of hair that makes it more receptive to the absorption of a tint.

Powder Bleach . . . . A strong, fast-acting lightener used for special lightening.

Pre-lightening . . . . The process of removing some color from the hair before a tint. Not necessary with Miss Clairol Hair Color Bath. The term is also used when highly decolorizing before applying the Blonde Toners.

Pre-softening . . . . . The application of a mild lightening solution for a short period of time in order to make hair more porous and less resistant to color. Not necessary with Miss Clairol Hair Color Bath.

Problem Hair . . . . Hair difficult to tint, lighten or permanent wave.

Reconditioning . . . . The process of improving the condition of the hair.

Resistance . . . . . The condition of hair that makes it difficult for solutions to penetrate the hair strand.

Retouch . . . . . . The process of coloring the new growth on tinted or lightened hair.

Rinse . . . . A temporary haircoloring such as Come Alive Gray.

**Semi-permanent
Haircoloring** . . . . . Haircoloring that lasts through several shampoos. Penetrates hair shaft slightly; does not coat hair as rinses 'do. Contains no peroxide and needs no peroxide to develop color.

Sensitivity . . . . . A skin highly reactive to the presence of a specific chemical. Skin reddens or becomes irritated shortly after application of the chemical. On removal of the chemical the reaction subsides. A sensitivity is not an allergy. (See allergy.)

Shampoo Tint . . . . A penetrating tint which contains, in addition to color, a superfine liquid shampoo that cleanses the hair as it colors.

Skin Test . . . . . . Same as Patch Test.

Soap Cap . . . . . . The process of diluting tint with shampoo or water and working it through the head like a shampoo.

Spot Lightening . . . . Applying lightener only to dark areas to even out color.

Spot Tinting . . . . . Applying tint to areas insufficiently colored in order to produce even results throughout.

Strand Test . . . . . A Preliminary Test given before a coloring treatment on a single strand of hair. It is used to predetermine the mixture and development time required during the treatment.

Streaking . . . . . Lightening from two to four strands at the hairline.

Streaks . . . . Dark or light areas on hair caused by improper application of tint or lightener.

Stripping . . . . . . The removal of artificial color from the hair.

Texture . . . . . . Refers to the thickness of hair and whether it is soft, harsh or wiry.

Tint . . . . A preparation which colors hair permanently.

Tipping . . . . . . Tiny strands of hair to the front of the head are lightened to blend in with the darker hair.

Towel Drying . . . . Removal of excess water with towel.

Vegetable Color . . . . A coloring which coats the hair and is derived from henna, sage or indigo.

Virgin Hair . . . . . Hair not previously treated with tints, lighteners or permanents.

White Henna . . . . . A magnesium carbonate added to hydrogen peroxide in order to thicken the lightener solution into a pack.

TRADEMARKS

The following are trademarks of Clairol Incorporated, Stamford, Connecticut, U.S.A.

BABY PEARL
BLACK PEARL
BLACK VELVET
BLUE LIGHTENING
BLUSH PEARL
BUTTERCUP BEIGE
CHAMPAGNE BEIGE
CHAMPAGNE ICE
CHAMPAGNE PARFAIT
CHAMPAGNE SHERBET
CHAMPAGNE TOAST
CHERRY SILVER
CHESTNUT BROWN
CLAIR-FILL
CLAIROL
CLAIROLITE
CLAIROXIDE
COFFEE BROWN
COLOR BATH
COLOR DIAL
COME ALIVE
COME ALIVE BLONDE
COME ALIVE BROWN
COME ALIVE GRAY
COME ALIVE RED
COPPERTONE
CREME TONER
CREMOGENIZED
DOES SHE...
  or DOESN'T SHE?
ERMINE
EXTRA-LITE A
EXTRA-LITE B
EXTRA-LITE SILVER
  BLONDE
EXTRA-LITE PLATINUM
FASHION COLORS
FASHION FOILS
FIRE SILVER
FLAXEN BLONDE
FLAME
GOLDEN APRICOT

HAIR COLOR BATH
HAIR COLOR SO
  NATURAL ONLY HER
  HAIRDRESSER KNOWS
  FOR SURE
HAIR SO NEW
HONEY BROWN
HONEY CHIFFON
INSTANT CLAIROL
INSTANT WHIP
IVORY CHIFFON
LADY CLAIROL
LIGHTENING BOOSTER
LOVING CARE
METALEX
MIDNIGHT OPAL
MINK BROWN
MISS AMIROL
MISS CLAIROL
MOONBEAM BLONDE
MOONGOLD
ONLY HER HAIRDRESSER
  KNOWS FOR SURE
PASTEL PEARL
PEACH CHIFFON
PINK CHIFFON
PINK SILVER
PLATINUM BEIGE
PROTINATOR
PURE WHITE
RED FASHION COLORS
RED GINGER
REMOV-ZIT
REP. OF A CROWN
  (FIVE POINT CROWN)
REP. OF AN ANGULAR
  CROWN
(THREE POINT CROWN)
ROSE BEIGE
RUSSET BROWN
SABLE BROWN

SALON FORMULA
10B SANDY BLONDE
SILK & SILVER
SILVER BEIGE
SILVER BLU
SILVER DIAMOND
SILVER DROPS
SILVER PLATINUM
SILVER SMOKE
SILVER MIST
SILVERY EXTRA WHITE
SILVERY PEARL
SILVERY PLATINUM
SILVERY SLATE
SILVERY SMOKE
SILVERY WHITE
SMOKE PLATINUM
SPARKLING COLOR
SPARKLING BLONDE
SPARKLING COPPER
SPARKLING DEEP AUBURN
SPARKLING DARK BROWN
SPARKLING LIGHT BROWN
SPARKLING MEDIUM AUBURN
SPARKLING MEDIUM BROWN
SPARKLING SHERRY
SPARKLING SILVER
STARLIGHT
STRAWBERRY BLONDE
STERLING PEARL
SUN BRONZE
SYLK
SUN SILVER
TAN PEARL
TAUPE PEARL
TITIAN BROWN
TOPAZ
9A TOWHEAD
ULTRA BLUE
VITAPOINTE
WHITE BEIGE
WHITE SAPPHIRE

247

INDEX